The MAILBOX®

The Education Center®

MATH

INDEPENDENT PRACTICE

SUPER SIMPLE!

grade **K**

EASY-TO-USE IDEAS FOR SKILL REINFORCEMENT

☑ Number sense

☑ Counting

☑ Measurement

☑ Addition & Subtraction

 Patter[n]

 Shapes

 Sorting

☑ **AND LOTS MORE!**

ENOUGH FOR

4 activities for every week

OF THE SCHOOL YEAR

Managing Editor: Lynn Drolet

Editorial Team: Becky S. Andrews, Randi Austin, Jennifer Avegno, Diane Badden, Kimberley Bruck, Karen A. Brudnak, Kitty Campbell, LeeAnn Collins, Pam Crane, Chris Curry, Stacie Stone Davis, Lynette Dickerson, Sarah Foreman, Bonnie Gaynor, Kathy Ginn, Theresa Lewis Goode, Ada Goren, Tazmen Hansen, Marsha Heim, Lori Z. Henry, Jodie Holman, Debra Liverman, Dorothy McKinney, Thad H. McLaurin, Sharon Murphy, Jennifer Nunn, Tina Petersen, Gerri Primak, Mark Rainey, Greg D. Rieves, Mary Robles, Hope Rodgers, Deborah Ryan, Leanne Swinson, Joshua Thomas, Allison E. Ward, Carole Watkins, Zane Williard

www.themailbox.com

Manufactured in the United States
10 9 8 7 6 5 4 3 2 1

Table of Contents

To use the table of contents as a checklist, make a copy of pages 2 and 3. Staple or clip each copy on top of its original page. Each time you use an activity, check its box. Start each school year with fresh copies of the pages.

Skills Index on pages 111-112.

Parade of Animals

Counting to 10

Materials:
large box with 10 stuffed animals
strip of tape (starting line)

A student counts aloud as she removes each animal from the box. Then she marches the first animal to the starting line of her parade and whispers, "One animal in the parade." She counts each remaining animal as she marches it to the parade lineup. Then she counts aloud to ten as she marches each animal along a parade route that ends inside the box.

Three animals in the parade.

Super Dots!

Number recognition

Materials:
student copies of a number outline, programmed as shown
bingo dauber (light color)

A youngster searches for the featured number inside of the number's outline. When he finds it, he uses the bingo dauber to dab it with a dot!

Apples Aplenty!

Sorting

Materials:
tree cutout
container of pom-poms (red, green, and yellow)

A child pours the pom-poms (apples) onto the tree cutout. Then she "picks" the apples from the tree and sorts them by color. For an added challenge, she counts the apples in each color and determines which color has the greatest number of apples. Then she draws on blank paper an apple tree that shows apples in that color.

Scoop by Scoop

One-to-one correspondence

Materials:
container with 10 sheets of paper, balled up (ice cream)
10 bowls
ice cream scooper

A student scoops one serving of ice cream into a bowl. He continues to place one scoop in each bowl. Then he pretends to eat each scoop of ice cream as he removes it from the bowl. He continues serving and eating ice cream in this manner as time permits.

Spaghetti and Meatballs

Counting to 10

Materials:
paper plate with red yarn lengths (spaghetti)
pot with 10 brown pom-poms (meatballs)
large spoon

A student says, "One," aloud as she spoons a meatball onto the plate of spaghetti. She continues in this manner, counting to ten, as she empties the pot. Then she counts aloud a second time as she pretends to eat each meatball. For more practice, she returns the meatballs to the pot and begins again.

Wiggly Worms

Length

Materials:
2 brown paper rectangles in different sizes (gardens)
even number of different yarn lengths (worms)

A child picks up two worms to compare their lengths. He drops the longer worm in the big garden and the shorter worm in the small garden. He continues in this manner until each worm is in a garden.

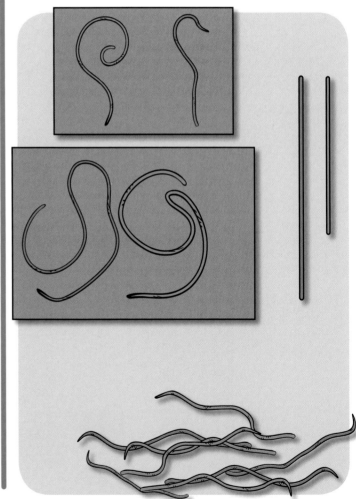

Found Treasure

Comparing sets

Materials:
treasure items
treasure box or paper bag

Possible treasure items include craft foam shapes, pattern blocks, dinosaur counters, farm-animal counters, and bear counters.

A youngster inspects the treasure and sorts it into piles. Then she counts to compare two of the piles, identifying which pile has less and which has more. She continues in this manner, comparing different sets of treasure as time permits.

There's less in this pile.

How Many Socks?

Graphing

Materials:
student copies of page 76 programmed with a title
student copies of the sock cards on page 77
2 different-color crayons
scissors
glue

A student uses one crayon to color a desired number of sock cards. She uses the other crayon to color the remaining cards. Next, she colors to label the graph with the two sock colors. She cuts out each sock card and glues it in the corresponding row of the graph. Then she compares her colorful results.

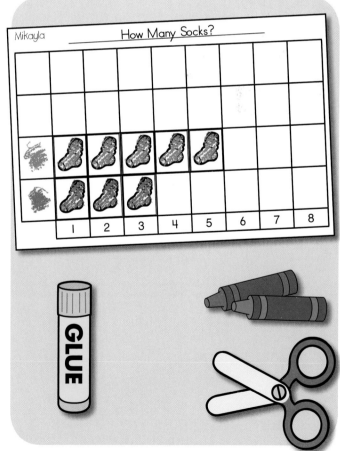

The Frame Shop

One-to-one correspondence

Materials:
several 3½" x 5" photographs or drawings
copies of the frame pattern on page 77
    (one per photograph)

A youngster places each frame faceup. Then he places one photograph in the center of each frame.

Piles of Geometry

Shapes

Materials:
copy of page 78, cut apart
supply of shapes

A child takes a shape and matches it to the shape shown on the corresponding card. He continues in this manner with each remaining shape. For an added challenge, he names each shape as he sorts.

Clipping Coupons

Counting to 10

Materials:
coupon flyers
envelopes (one per student)
scissors

A youngster looks through the flyers and cuts out coupons for products she likes. Each time she cuts out a coupon, she counts to find her total number of coupons. When she has ten coupons, she counts aloud as she places each coupon in her envelope.

Mixed Pairs

Equivalent sets

Materials:
sets of objects, with an equal number of objects in every two sets

Possible matching sets include three pencils and three blocks, five erasers and five books, two stuffed animals and two caps.

A student sorts the objects into sets. Then he counts the number of objects in each set. Next, he matches each set to the set with an equal number of objects. For an added challenge, he draws on paper one pair of equal sets.

Card Connections

Number matching

Materials:
copy of page 79, cut apart
number cards 1–12

A child shuffles each set of cards and places them faceup in his work space. Then he finds the match for each number and puts one atop the other. For an added challenge, he puts the pairs in numerical order.

Squares for Bears

One-to-one correspondence

Materials:
desired number of paper squares
teddy bear counters

A student arranges the squares in a circle. Next, she places a bear on each square. For an added challenge, set out an unequal number of squares and counters and have students determine if there are enough bears to put one on every square.

Super Simple Independent Practice: Math • ©The Mailbox® Books • TEC61153

City Skyline

Height

Materials:
Unifix cubes
die
blank paper
crayons

A youngster rolls the die and connects the matching number of Unifix cubes to make a tower. Then he rolls the die again and connects the corresponding number of cubes to make a second tower. He compares the towers' heights and traces the taller one on his paper. He continues in this manner to create a skyline on his paper.

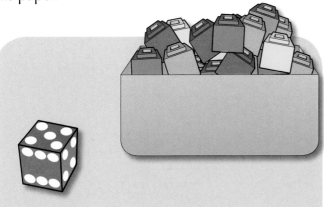

Chain Trains

Comparing sets

Materials:
math links, a different number of links in each of 4 colors

To make each train, a student connects same-color math links. Then she compares the lengths of the trains to find the longest and shortest trains. For an added challenge, she traces the longest and shortest trains on a sheet of paper.

Passport, Please!

Counting to 10

Materials:
student copies of the passport on page 80
stampers (or stickers)
ink pad
crayons

After personalizing his passport, a child chooses stamps to make prints on his passport. Each time he makes a print, he counts his total number of prints. When he has a total of ten prints, he sets the stamps aside and counts aloud as he points to each print.

Under Cover

Number identification

Materials:
number strip from 1 to 6
6 counters
die

A student rolls the die and counts the number of dots. Then she places a counter on the corresponding number on the strip. She continues to roll the die until each number on the strip has been identified. For more practice, she removes the corresponding counter for each number rolled.

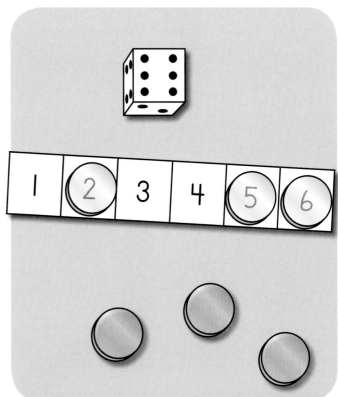

Pretty Petals

Matching sets

Materials:
copy of the flower petals on page 80, cut out
flower cutout, without petals
dice
blank paper
crayons

A youngster rolls the dice. For each dot on each die rolled, she places a petal on the flower. Then she draws the flower on her blank paper. To finish, she draws seeds in the center of her flower to show the total number of dots rolled.

Gather Round

Shapes

Materials:
round paper plates (one per student)
magazines
scissors
glue

A student looks through magazines to find pictures of circles and round objects. When a picture is found, he identifies the circle and cuts it out. Then he glues his cutout to his plate. He continues in this manner to create a collage.

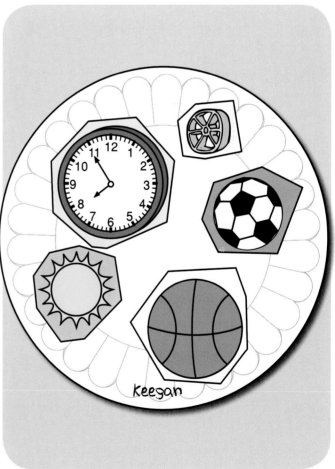

Happy Hoppers

Sorting

Materials:
several copies of the frog cards on page 81, cut out
3 log cutouts

A youngster takes a frog card and pretends to make it jump on a log. Then she takes a different frog and determines if it is the same size as the frog on the log. If the frog is the same size, she makes it hop on the same log. If the frog is a different size, she makes it hop on a different log. She continues to sort each frog card in this manner as time permits.

Loopy Loops

Equivalent sets

Materials:
dominoes
stickers
bingo dauber
blank paper
crayons

A student identifies each set of dots on a domino. He uses the bingo dauber to make equivalent sets on the top and bottom of his paper to match the domino. Next, he uses stickers and his own drawings to make equivalent sets across his paper. Then he draws a loop around each completed set as shown.

Little Florist

Length

Materials:
6 copies of the flower patterns on page 81, cut out
artificial flower with stem
24 pipe cleaners (stems), each taped to a flower (12 stems longer and 12 stems shorter than the artificial flower)

A student compares the length of each prepared flower to the artificial flower. She places the longer flowers in one bundle and places the shorter flowers in a second bundle. If desired, provide plastic vases for her sorted bouquets.

This flower is shorter.

A Fuzzy Row

Number writing

Materials:
resealable plastic bags, each with a different number of pom-poms
blank paper
crayons

A student opens a bag and arranges the pom-poms to make a row on his paper. Then he counts aloud as he numbers each pom-pom. He continues in this manner with each remaining bag.

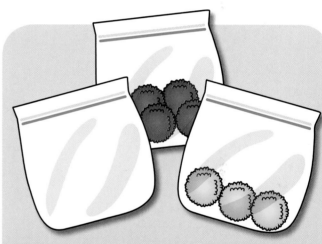

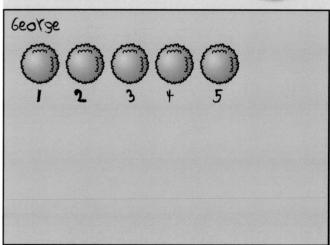

George

1 2 3 4 5

Search and Find

One-to-one correspondence

Materials:
student copies of the recording sheet on page 82
dominoes
dice

    A child rolls the dice. Then she looks for a domino with halves that correspond to the number of dots on each die. If a match is made, she draws the dice and domino dots on her recording sheet. If a match is not made, she rolls again. She continues in this manner to complete her paper.

In the Ocean

Number identification

Materials:
student copies of the fish cards on page 82
cards programmed as shown
blue construction paper (one per student)
scissors
crayons
glue

    A student identifies the color of the fish and the number on each programmed card and colors a corresponding number of fish cards to match. Then he cuts out his fish cards and glues them to the blue paper (ocean). He embellishes his paper with ocean details as time permits.

Around the Dinosaur

Positional words

Materials:
student copies of page 83
cards programmed as shown
blank paper
scissors
crayons
glue

A youngster cuts out his dinosaur and glues it in the center of his paper. Then he draws something above, below, and next to his dinosaur. To complete the activity, he labels his pictures with the corresponding positional words.

Yum, Yum!

Sorting

Materials:
3 copies of page 84, cut out and colored as shown
supply of red, blue, and brown pom-poms

A student uses the muffin liner color to identify each type of muffin: cranberry, blueberry, or chocolate chip. Then she sorts the red pom-poms on the cranberry muffin, the blue pom-poms on the blueberry muffin, and the brown pom-poms on the chocolate chip muffin.

Lots o' Chips

Making sets

Materials:
small paper bags (one per student)
number cards from 1 to 10
circle cutouts
crayons

A youngster writes his name on a paper bag and takes a card. He copies the number on one side of a circle (cookie) and then draws the corresponding number of dots (chocolate chips) on the other side. Then he drops his cookie in his bag. He continues to make more cookies with different cards as time permits.

Train Tracks

Length

Materials:
black paper strips of different lengths (train tracks) labeled with letters
toy train (or a picture of a train)
blank paper
crayons

A child makes a T chart on her paper. She labels one column with a happy face and the other with a sad face. Next, she places the train on a track. If the train fits on the track, she writes the corresponding letter below the happy face on her T chart. If the train does not fit, she records the letter below the sad face. She continues in this manner for each remaining train track.

Sequenced Strips

Number order

Materials:
cards numbered from 1 to 10, folded as shown
sentence strips (one per student)

A student places the cards in a line showing the correct number order. Then he copies the numbers on his sentence strip. For an added challenge, he orders and writes the numbers in reverse order.

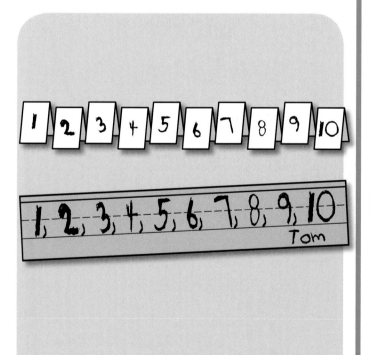

Spinning for Colors

Graphing

Materials:
student copies of page 76, programmed
    with a title and spinner colors
color spinner
crayons

A student spins the spinner and identifies the color on which it lands. She colors the corresponding box on her graph to record her first spin. Then she continues to spin, recording the data in the same manner to "race" the colors. The first color to reach the eighth box on her grid is declared the winner.

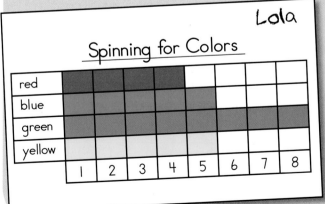

More or Less

Comparing sets

Materials:
copy of the comparison word cards
  on page 85, cut apart
construction paper with dividing line
Unifix cubes
die

A student rolls the die and places the matching number of Unifix cubes on one half of the paper. Then she rolls the die again and places that number of Unifix cubes on the other half. After comparing the two numbers, she puts the word cards in the appropriate places. Then she removes the cubes and cards and repeats the activity as time allows.

Ten Little Fingers

Number order

Materials:
2 extra large hand cutouts
yellow strips glued to make rings,
  numbered from 1 to 10
blank paper
crayons

A student takes the number 1 ring and places it on the far left finger of the first cutout. He continues placing the rings on the fingers, moving from left to right. After he counts to ten, he traces two hands on his paper. Then he writes on the fingers the numbers 1 to 10.

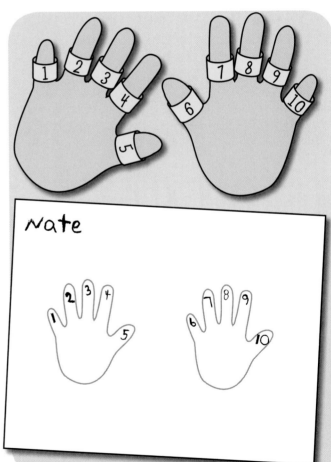

On or Off?

Positional words

Materials:
table cutouts (one per student)
magazines
blank paper
glue
scissors

A student glues a table cutout to her paper and writes "on" and "off" in appropriate places. Next, she cuts out magazine pictures of things that would be on a table and glues them in place. Then she cuts out pictures of things that would be off the table and glues them in place.

Happy Birthday!

Matching sets

Materials:
student copies of the recording sheet on page 85
6 birthday candles
play dough
die
crayons

A student makes a cake using his play dough. When he has formed his cake to his liking, he rolls the die and places a matching number of candles in the cake. Next, he writes the number beside the first cake on his recording sheet and draws the corresponding number of candles. Then he repeats the activity three times to complete his paper.

Picture Perfect

Graphing

Materials:
pocket chart, labeled as shown
individual student photos
2 bingo daubers (different colors)
construction paper (one sheet per student)

A student places the photos in the appropriate columns of the pocket chart. Then she folds a sheet of construction paper in half lengthwise and labels the columns to match the pocket chart. Next, she counts the number of girls and uses a bingo dauber to make the corresponding number of dots on the correct side of her paper. Then she counts the number of boys and uses the other bingo dauber to mark her paper. Finally, she adds details to the dots to make faces.

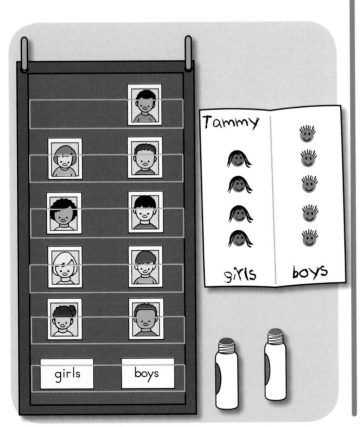

Ocean Creatures

Making sets

Materials:
copy of the picture cards on page 86, cut apart
cube labeled with any six numbers
12" x 18" sheets of light blue construction
    paper (one per student)
scissors
crayons

A student cuts the top of his paper (ocean) to look like waves. Next, he rolls the cube and chooses a picture card. He then draws in his ocean the correct number of the animal shown on the card and writes the number from the cube near the drawings. He rolls the cube again and repeats the process for each remaining card.

Lots of Dots

Comparing sets

Materials:
dominoes
paper rectangles
blank paper
markers
crayons
glue

A student uses a marker to draw dots on a rectangle to match a chosen domino. Next, he lightly colors the half of his domino that has more dots. Then he glues his domino to his paper. He continues making dominoes in this manner as time allows.

"Dino-mite" Designs

Patterns

Materials:
tagboard cutout copies of page 83,
    programmed with pattern starters as shown
different-colored clothespins to match the patterns

A student chooses a dinosaur and places matching clothespins on the colored dots. Then she continues the pattern across the back of the dinosaur. She repeats this process for each dinosaur.

Here's the Scoop

Comparing sets

Materials:
student copies of the word cards on page 85
triangle cutouts (two per student)
small tagboard ice cream scoop tracer
12" x 18" sheets of construction paper
    (one per student)
die
scissors
crayons
glue

A student folds her paper in half lengthwise, unfolds it, and glues two triangles (ice cream cones) at the bottom of each side. Next, she rolls the die and traces a matching number of scoops above one cone. Then she rolls the die again and traces that number of scoops above the other cone. Next, she cuts apart her word cards and glues the appropriate card to each cone.

Caterpillar Crossing

Measurement

Materials:
2" lengths of pipe cleaners (caterpillars)
brown paper strips (branches) in the following lengths:
    4", 8", 10", 12", 14", and 18"

A student chooses a tree branch. To find out how many caterpillars fit on the branch, he places caterpillars end to end across the branch. Next, he counts the number of caterpillars on the branch. The student repeats the activity with the remaining branches.

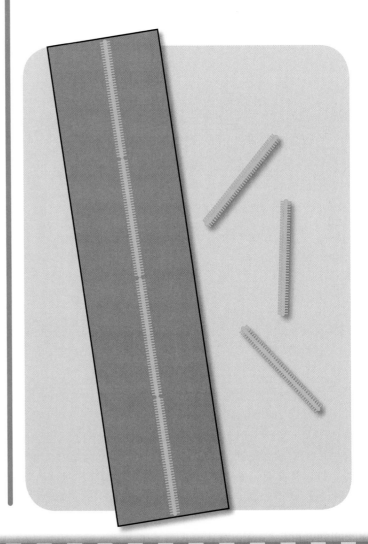

Flatware Fun

Sorting

Materials:
supply of plastic flatware
flatware tray (optional)
blank paper

A student sorts the flatware by type. Next, she draws on her paper a picture of each type of flatware. Then, for each set, she counts and records the total number next to each drawing.

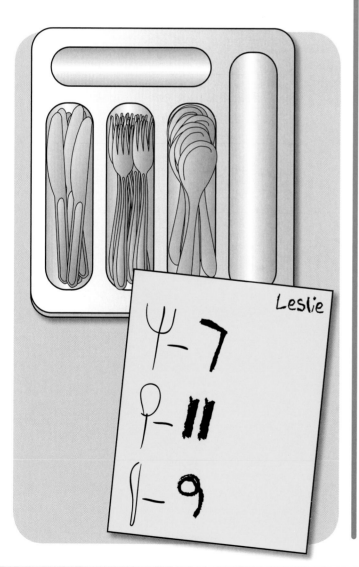

Blast Off!

Counting backward

Materials:
copy of the rocket pattern on page 86, cut out and glued to a craft stick
number cards from 1 to 10

The student places the cards in order and counts to check his work. Then he counts backward, touching each card with the rocket as he says the number. When he arrives at 1, he quietly pretends to make his rocket "blast off." He repeats the activity as time allows.

Striped Snakes

Patterns

Materials:
pattern starters made with Unifix cubes
paper rectangles in colors to match Unifix cubes
paper strips
scissors
crayons
glue

    To make a snake, a student glues rectangles on his paper strip to match a chosen pattern. He continues to extend the pattern to the end of the strip. Then he makes the head by adding details to the first rectangle. To finish his snake, he rounds each of the four corners of his strip. He repeats this activity with other pattern starters as time allows.

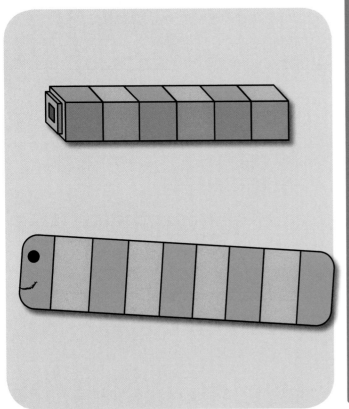

More Spots

Comparing sets

Materials:
copy of the word comparison cards
    on page 85, cut apart
several copies of the dog pattern on
    page 87, cut out and programmed
    with different numbers of spots
blank copy of the dog pattern on page 87, cut out
black pom-poms

    A student counts the spots on a chosen dog. Then she chooses a word card and puts a corresponding number of pom-poms (spots) on the blank dog. After counting to confirm her answer, she removes the spots and repeats the activity with the other dogs.

More than

Sky or Grass?

Sorting

Materials:
student copies of page 88
12" x 18" sheets of construction paper
    (one per student)
scissors
crayons
glue

A student lightly colors the top part of his paper blue (sky) and the bottom part green (grass). Next, he cuts apart his picture cards and glues them in the appropriate areas.

Color That Roll!

Graphing

Materials:
student copies of the graph on page 76,
    labeled with a title and labels as shown
die
crayons

A student rolls the die and counts the number of dots. Then she colors a matching number of spaces beside "Roll 1" on her graph. She continues this process to complete the graph, using a different crayon for each roll. To finish, she draws a smiley face next to the line with the most squares colored.

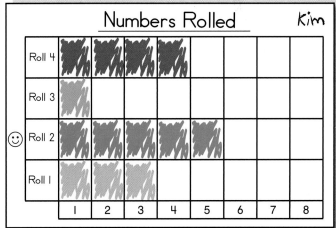

Priority Mail

Sorting

Materials:
several pieces of mail in various categories
large pillowcase (mailbag)

Possible categories of mail include letters, boxes, magazines, coupons, advertisements, and flyers.

A student pretends to be a mail carrier and empties the mailbag. Then he sorts each piece of mail by category. For an added challenge, he re-sorts each pile into subcategories, such as different names of magazines.

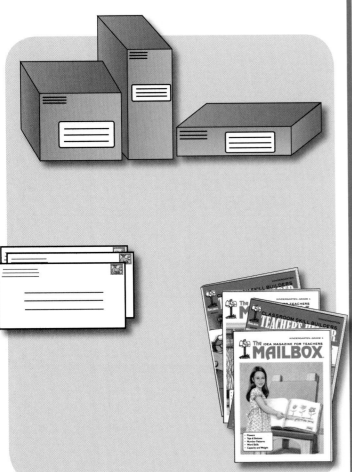

Laundered Load

Counting

Materials:
basket with washcloths, unfolded

A youngster removes washcloths from the basket and folds them. Each time she folds a washcloth, she counts the number of folded items. When she has folded each of the washcloths, she counts aloud as she returns each one to the basket.

Best Buddies

Positional words

Materials:
paper strips programmed as shown (one per student)
blank paper
crayons

A student reads the sentence. He writes a desired name on the blank to complete the sentence and then glues the strip on his paper. Then he draws and labels a picture to illustrate his sentence.

Stamps Galore!

Comparing sets

Materials:
student copies of the comparison
    word cards on page 85
stampers
ink pads
blank paper
scissors
glue

A child folds her paper to make four boxes and then stamps a desired number of prints in the first box. Next, she cuts apart her word cards and glues one card in each of the remaining boxes. To complete each labeled box, she stamps the appropriate number of prints as compared to the first box. For an added challenge, she writes the number of objects in the corner of each box.

Inch by Inch

Measurement

Materials:
student copies of page 89
supply of 1" paper squares
12" x 18" sheet of paper (one per student)
scissors
glue

A youngster cuts apart her snake cards. Next, she glues a snake on her paper. She arranges the paper squares below the snake to measure it from end to end and then glues them in place. Then she records the length of the snake. She continues in this manner with each remaining snake.

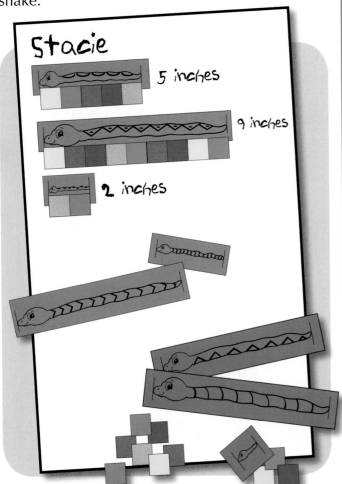

Savvy About Seasons

Calendar

Materials:
copy of page 90, cut apart
season strips, similar to the ones shown

A student uses the season strips as headers for each of four columns. Then he identifies the time of year on a chosen card and places it in the corresponding column. He continues in this manner with each remaining card. To extend the activity, he writes a sentence about his favorite season.

Where Is It?

Positional words

Materials:
student copies of the dog pattern on page 87
cards programmed as shown (for reference)
blank paper
scissors
crayons
glue

A youngster draws a bridge on her paper. She cuts out her dog pattern and glues it on the bridge. Next, she draws something under the bridge. Then she draws something over and next to her dog. To complete the activity, she writes to label her pictures with the corresponding positional words.

Beachcomber

Counting to 15

Materials:
tagboard copy of the shell cards on page 87, cut apart
tub of sand
small shovel
colander

A student counts aloud as she buries each shell card in the sand. Then she holds the colander over the tub and pours a shovelful of sand into the colander. She removes each shell, if any, and counts the number of shells. She continues to scoop sand, recounting the shells after each scoop, as time permits.

Corners and Sides

Shape identification

Materials:
craft sticks (seven per child)
pom-poms (seven per child)
crayons
glue

A student arranges his craft sticks to form a square and a triangle. Then he colors each shape with its own unique design. He glues the sticks in place and glues a pom-pom on each shape's corners. For an added challenge, he writes the number of sides and corners for each shape.

City Skyscrapers

Sorting

Materials:
6 different-color sets of Unifix cubes, ranging from 1 to 8 cubes per set
labeled graph paper similar to the one shown (on display)
sheets of 1" graph paper (one per student)
crayons

A student labels her graph paper to match the one on display. Then she sorts the cubes by color, counts each pile, and colors the corresponding boxes on her graph paper. She traces on her graph each color bar (skyscraper) to complete her city skyline.

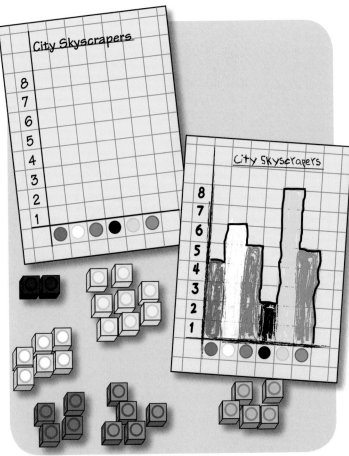

Scoot!

Number order

Materials:
number cards from 1 to 20

A student searches to find the number 10 card and puts it in the middle of her workspace. Next, she picks up a different card, determines its numerical order in reference to the number 10, and lays it down. She continues with each remaining card, scooting the cards as necessary, until all 20 cards are in sequential order. Then she counts aloud as she points to each number.

More Cookies

Comparing sets

Materials:
number cards from 1 to 10
cookie sheet
play dough
blank paper
crayons

A student places two cards on the cookie sheet. She places the corresponding number of play dough cookies next to each card. Next, she draws a picture showing the number cards and cookies. Then she circles the set with more cookies. She removes the materials from the cookie sheet and repeats the activity with two different cards.

Clouds Adrift

Counting to 20

Materials:
large sheet of blue construction paper (sky)
20 cotton balls

A child counts each cotton ball (cloud). Then she counts again as she places each cloud on the sky to form a puffy cloud picture. When all 20 clouds are in the picture, she pretends to be the wind and blows the clouds apart. She continues in this manner, making different scenes in the sky as time permits.

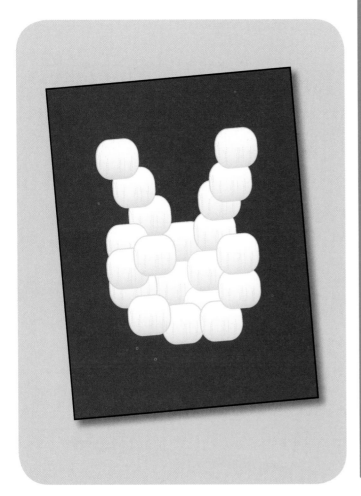

Supreme Pizza

Graphing

Materials:
student copies of page 76, labeled with the title shown
student copies of page 91
scissors
crayons
glue

A youngster cuts out her pizza. Then she cuts apart her cards and glues them on her graph to label her rows. Next, she colors on her pizza one of the four types of toppings, counts the items, and colors her graph to record her results. She continues with each remaining topping in the same manner. For an added challenge, she writes a sentence that tells about her graph.

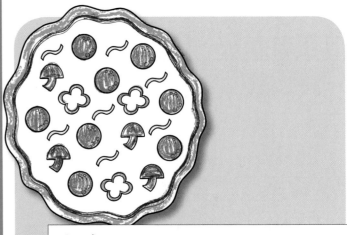

Comb the Room

Length

Materials:
a clean comb
blank paper
crayons

A student makes a T chart on blank paper and labels each column as shown. Next, he searches the room for objects that are longer than and shorter than the comb. He draws different objects in the corresponding columns as time permits.

Bugs on a Log

Concept of addition

Materials:
2 sets of number cards, from 0 to 5
rectangular cutout (log)
10 pom-poms, 5 each of 2 different colors (bugs)

A child takes a number card. She takes the corresponding number of one color of bugs and places them on the log. Next, she takes a card from the second number set. She places the corresponding number of the other color of bugs on the log. Then she counts the total number of bugs on the log.

Set 17

Side by Side

Positional words

Materials:
stickers
blank paper
crayons

A youngster folds his paper to make four sections. He chooses four stickers and places one in each section. Then he draws a picture *next to* each sticker. He adds details to his completed paper as time permits.

A Sunny Day

Patterns

Materials:
large yellow circle (sun)
yellow strips, short and long (sun's rays)
blank paper
crayons

A student arranges the short and long rays around the sun to make a pattern. Then she draws on her paper the resulting sun, taking care to copy the rays' pattern. She embellishes her paper with details as time permits.

Gumballs Galore

Comparing numbers

Materials:
2 copies of the gumball machine pattern
    on page 92, cut out
student copies of the recording sheet on page 92
supply of pom-poms (gumballs)
crayons

A child takes a handful of gumballs in each hand. She places each handful on a different gumball machine. Then she counts the number of gumballs for each machine and writes the total on her recording sheet as shown. She colors the gumball globes according to the color code. She continues in this manner to complete her paper.

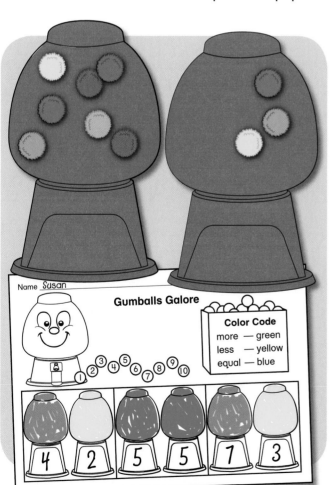

A Row of Gold

Number order

Materials:
long paper strips accordion-folded to make 20
    spaces (one per student)
20 yellow construction paper circles numbered
    1–20 (coins)
crayons

A student places the coins faceup on a work surface. Next, he arranges the coins in numerical order. He counts aloud and checks the order of the coins. When the coins are in numerical order, he copies each number onto his strip.

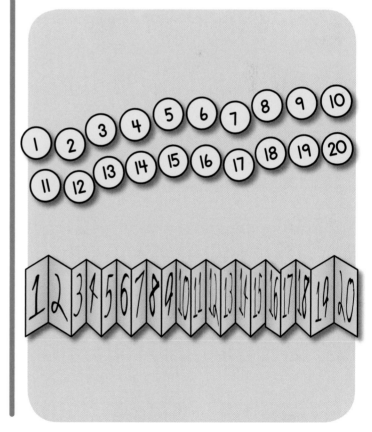

Human Scale

Comparing weights

Materials:
tub of heavy objects
tub of light objects

Possible heavy objects include a book, a block, and a full box of crayons. Possible light objects include a feather, a clean tissue, and a sheet of paper.

A student removes one item from each tub. She stands with her arms outstretched, holding one item in each hand. Then she imitates a scale by tipping the heavier object downward and the lighter object upward. She continues in this manner with different items as time permits. For an added challenge, have her draw herself holding two chosen items in her final pose.

Hop on Top

Comparing numbers

Materials:
2 copies of page 79, cut apart
large bear counter
small bear counter

A youngster shuffles the cards and places the deck facedown. He flips the top two cards and places them side by side. Then he pretends to make the large bear hop on the larger number and the small bear hop on the smaller number. If the flipped cards are equal, he stacks the cards and pretends to make both bears hop on top! He continues in this manner with the remaining cards.

Fish's Bubbles

Concept of addition

Materials:
student copies of the fish pattern on page 93
light blue paper (one per student)
2 bingo daubers of different colors
die
scissors
crayons
glue

A student cuts out her fish and glues it to her paper. Next, she rolls the die and uses one bingo dauber to make the corresponding number of dots above her fish. She rolls the die again and uses the other bingo dauber to make the matching number of dots. Then she writes the total number of her fish's bubbles on her paper. For an added challenge, she uses the bubbles to write an addition sentence.

A Sorted Collection

Identifying shapes

Materials:
shapes in different sizes
cards labeled as shown

A student takes a shape and counts the number of sides. Then he places it by the corresponding card. He continues to sort each shape in this manner, saying each shape's name aloud. For an added challenge, he re-sorts each pile by size and shape.

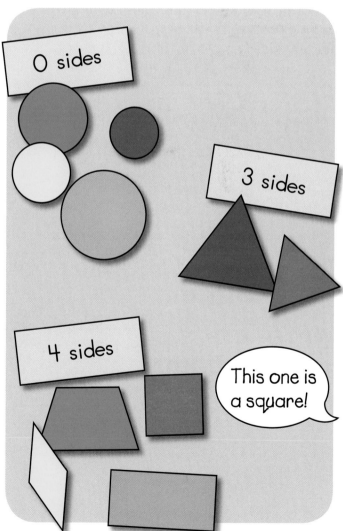

Pigs in Puddles

Concept of addition

Materials:
12 pink pom-poms (pigs)
2 green paper cutouts (pastures)
brown paper cutout (mud hole)
dice

A student rolls the dice. Next, he counts aloud as he places the corresponding number of pigs for each die on a different pasture. Then he counts aloud to determine the total number of pigs as he walks each pig into the mud hole. He removes the pigs and rolls again for more rounds as time permits.

Animal Travels

Sorting

Materials:
student copies of page 94, cut apart
2 plastic hoops, overlapped to make
    a Venn diagram, labeled as shown

A student looks at the card collection and determines how each animal travels. Then she sorts the cards into the corresponding spaces in the plastic hoops. For an added challenge, she copies the diagram on a sheet of paper and draws different animals in each category.

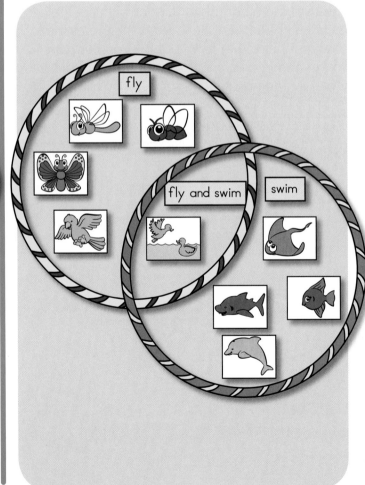

Seek and Find

Shape identification

Materials:
magazines
blank paper
scissors
crayons
glue

A student folds her paper to make three columns and labels them with shapes, as shown. Then she looks through magazines to find pictures of objects that correspond with the shapes on her paper. For each shape that she identifies, she cuts out the picture and glues it in the corresponding column.

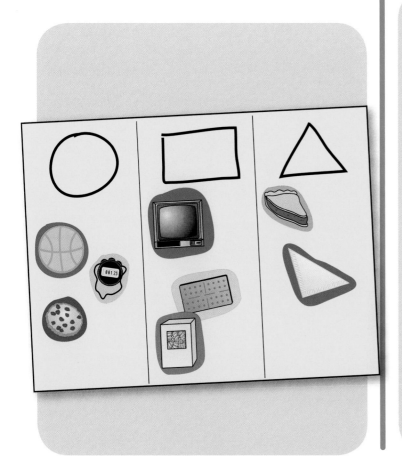

A Detailed Inspection

Collecting data

Materials:
student copies of page 95
various classroom objects
crayons

Possible classroom objects include a watered plant, a ball, an eraser, sandpaper, a stuffed animal, a carpet square, and a rock.

A student inspects a desired object to determine its attributes. She checks off her findings on her recording sheet. Then she draws on her paper the object described in the box.

Mice Prints

Patterns

Materials:
2 ink pads in different colors
wet paper towel
paper strips
fine-tip markers

A youngster makes inked fingerprints on her paper to create a color pattern. To transform each print into a mouse, she draws eyes, ears, a nose, a mouth, whiskers, and a tail. She continues to make more patterns on different strips as time permits.

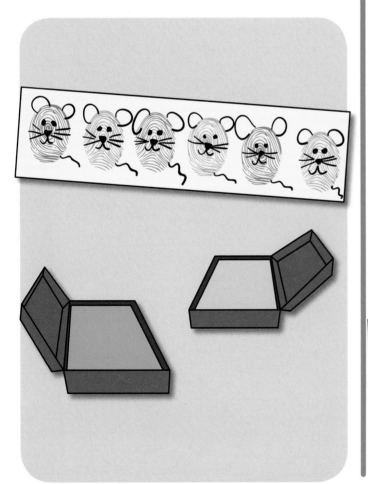

Taking Flight

Counting backward

Materials:
copies of the bird cards on page 93, cut apart
brown paper strip (branch)

A child counts aloud as he places the birds on the branch. He whispers, "Ten birds want to fly." Then he takes a bird and "flies" it off of the branch. He continues in this manner with each remaining bird, counting backward as each bird takes flight.

6 birds want to fly.

Bear's Barbells

Comparing lengths

Materials:
copy of page 96
cards labeled as shown
straws cut in different lengths (barbells)

A child takes a barbell and compares it to the length of the bear's barbell. She places the barbell by the corresponding card. She continues in this manner with each remaining barbell.

Two Scoops

Comparing numbers

Materials:
supply of large pom-poms
ice cream scooper
blank paper

A student folds his paper to make eight sections. Next, he gets two scoops of pom-poms, counts the total number of pom-poms in each scoop, and writes both numbers in the first section. Then he circles the larger number and underlines the smaller number. If the numbers are equal, he draws an equal sign between them. He returns the pom-poms to the supply and continues in this manner with two different scoops for each remaining section.

Monster's Munchies

Shapes

Materials:
copy of page 97, cut apart
supply of circles, squares, triangles, and rectangles
blank paper
crayons

A youngster identifies each monster's featured shape. Next, she pretends to feed each monster its favorite snack as she sorts each shape in the supply. For each shape fed, she says in a monster voice, "Thank you for the [shape]." Then she draws on her paper a chosen monster munching on its favorite snack!

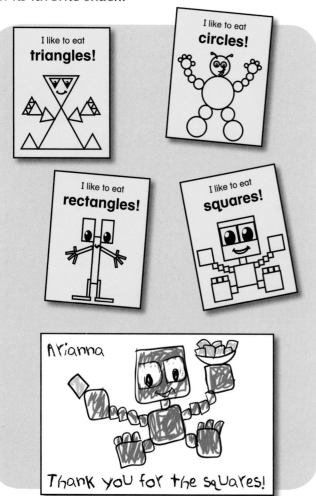

ABCs and 123s

Sorting

Materials:
magnetic letters and numbers
cookie sheet or other magnetic surface
blank paper
crayons

A student places the magnetic letters on one half of the cookie sheet and the numbers on the other. He folds his paper in half and draws each group on a different half. For an added challenge, the student chooses another way to sort the letters and numbers, such as by color or by whether they have straight lines. Then he draws these groups on the back of his paper.

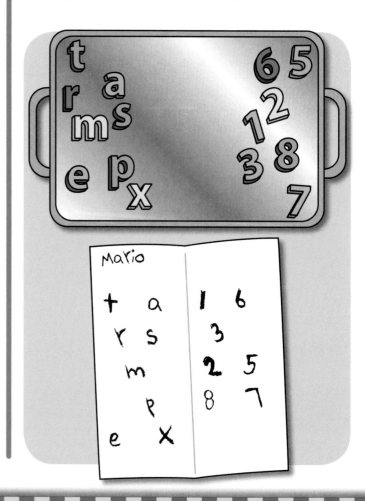

Nifty Names

Comparing numbers

Materials:
list of names, prepared as shown

A student counts the letters in a classmate's first name and writes the number in the box. Then he counts the letters in the last name and records the number. Next, he circles the name that contains more letters. If the first and last names contain the same amount of letters, he circles both names. He continues in the same manner for each name.

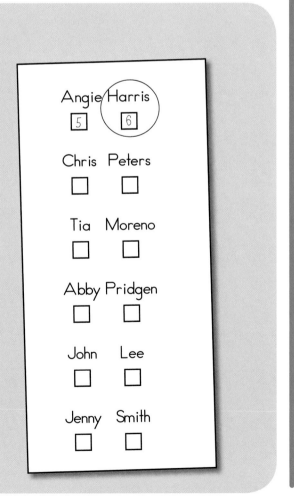

All Wrapped Up!

Weight

Materials:
several objects with different weights

Possible objects include a feather, an eraser, a stuffed animal, a rock, a book, and a paperweight.

A student compares two objects at a time to determine which is heavier and which is lighter. She arranges the objects, from lightest to heaviest, in a line. Then she confirms her findings by comparing the objects all the way down the line. For an added challenge, she draws a picture of her finished line and notes any surprises.

Set 22

Clip It!

Addition

Materials:
10 paper plates labeled with addition problems
clothespins in two different colors
blank paper

A student takes a plate and reads the math problem. For each addend, he uses a different-color clothespin and clips the corresponding number of pins to the plate. Then he counts the total number of clothespins to solve the problem and writes on his paper the completed number sentence. He continues in this manner with each remaining plate.

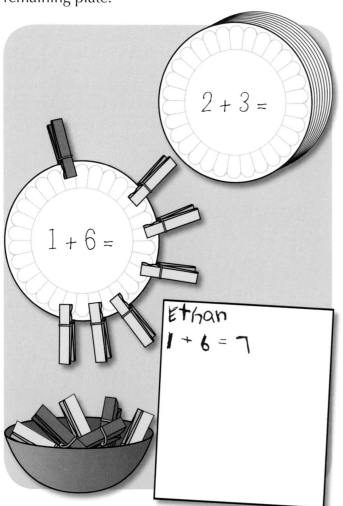

Use Your Noodles

Patterns

Materials:
supply of dry noodles, 3 different kinds
cards programmed with patterns,
    such as the ones shown
blank strips
glue

A youngster selects a card and identifies the pattern. Then she arranges noodles on her blank strip to copy and extend the pattern. After she checks her work, she glues the pieces in place. She continues with more pattern cards as time permits.

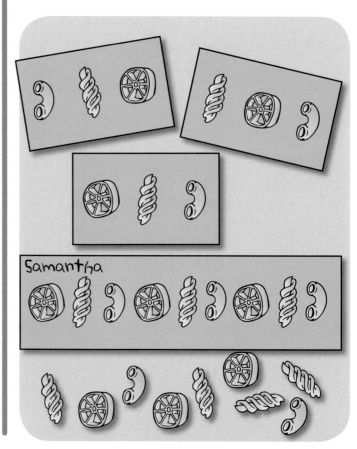

School Tools

Counting to 30

Materials:
backpack packed with 30 school tools

Possible school tools include pencils, crayons, glue sticks, rulers, scissors, erasers, and markers.

To unpack the backpack, a student removes one item at a time. For each item removed, she counts the number of school tools out of the backpack. When the backpack is empty, she counts aloud as she repacks each tool.

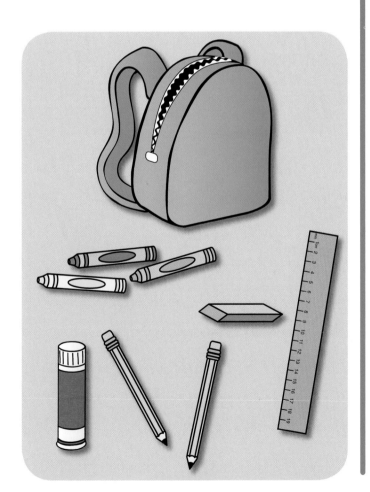

Buzzy's Travels

Measurement

Materials:
student copies of page 98
10 Unifix cubes

A child uses the cubes to measure the distance between Buzzy the Bee and each item on the map. He records each measurement by the corresponding pictures on the bottom of his paper.

In the Pond

Graphing

Materials:
student copies of page 76, programmed as shown
4 copies of the frog cards on page 81, cut out
large pond cutout topped with frog cards
crayons

A student identifies the three different sizes of frogs in the pond. He counts the number of frogs in each category; then he colors his graph to match. For an added challenge, have him write on the back of his paper a sentence about his graph.

Rolling and Recording

Shapes

Materials:
cube labeled with the numbers 0, 3, 3, 4, 4, 4
supply of shapes
blank paper
crayons

A youngster folds and labels her paper as shown. Then she rolls the cube and identifies the number that lands faceup. She finds a shape with the same number of sides as the number rolled and draws it in the corresponding column on her paper. She continues to roll and draw as time permits.

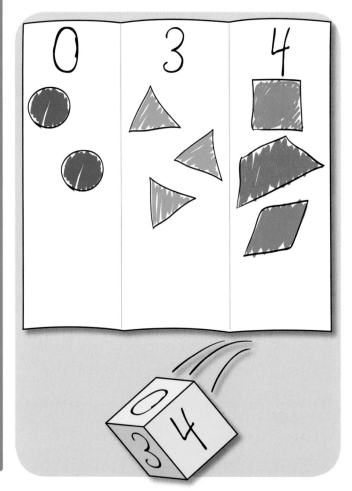

Cards and Dots

Making sets

Materials:
playing cards, face cards removed
blank paper

A child folds his paper and then unfolds it to make eight sections. For each section, he counts the number of large objects on a chosen card and writes the number on his paper. Then he makes the corresponding number of dots next to the number.

Bitty Bugs

Addition to 10

Materials:
strips of green construction paper
fine-tip marker
ink pad
blank paper
scissors
glue

A student fringe-cuts one long side of her green paper so it resembles grass and glues it to her blank paper. Then she makes two sets of fingerprints, with no more than five prints per set, and writes the number of prints above each set. She adds details to each print to make a bug. She completes her paper by writing a number sentence that corresponds with her buggy prints.

Set 24

How Many Blocks?

Weight

Materials:
balance scale
supply of blocks, same size and weight
different objects, varied weights

Objects might include a marker, an eraser, a stapler, a toy truck, a box of crayons, and a book.

A child places one object on one side of the scale and places one block at a time on the other side until the scale is balanced. Then, she places the object and the corresponding blocks together in her workspace. She repeats this process for each remaining object. Then she counts the blocks and uses her findings to arrange the objects from lightest to heaviest.

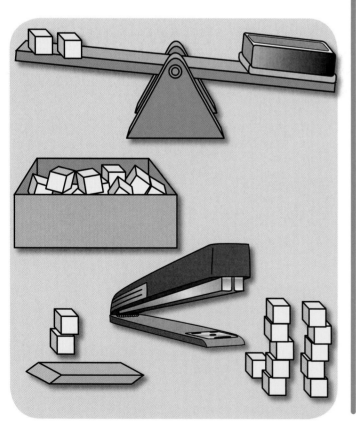

Butter the Popcorn

Number identification

Materials:
student copies of the popcorn grid on page 99, labeled with desired numbers from 0–30
number cards to 30
yellow crayon

A youngster takes a number card and identifies the number. Then, on his popcorn grid, he colors the same number, as if to butter his popcorn. If the number is not on his grid, he writes the number on the back of his paper. He continues in this manner with each remaining number card.

Silly Sevens

Addition to 12

Materials:
two dice
blank paper
crayons

A student rolls the dice and writes a number sentence that corresponds with the roll. If the sum of her roll is seven, she decorates the number sentence to make it look as silly as possible and then rolls again. If the sum does not equal seven, she rolls the dice to begin a new round.

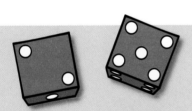

Kendra

$4 + 2 = 6$

$3 + 5 = 8$

$4 + 3 = 7$

$5 + 6 = 11$

$2 + 5 = 7$

Snazzy Snakes

Patterns

Materials:
construction paper rectangles
scissors
crayons

A student rounds the edges of the rectangle to make a snake shape and adds simple details to make a face. Then he creates a pattern across the back of the snake. He continues in this manner, making more snakes as time permits.

Set 26

Tiny Toes

Counting to 30

Materials:
student copies of page 100
fingerpaints
12" x 18" sheets of construction paper (one per student)
scissors
glue

A youngster cuts out the paw patterns and glues them to his paper so they resemble animal tracks. For each paw, he makes five fingerprint dots to make toes. Then he counts all his toes. For an added challenge, he counts by fives to 30.

George

A Photo Finish

Collecting data

Materials:
student copies of the sentence recording
    sheet on page 101
class photograph

A child reviews each question on her recording sheet. Then she looks at the photograph to answer each question. For an added challenge, she uses the information to complete a programmed graph.

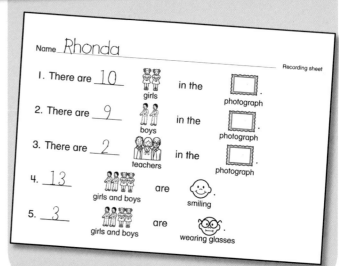

Name Rhonda

Recording sheet

1. There are 10 girls in the photograph.

2. There are 9 boys in the photograph.

3. There are 2 teachers in the photograph.

4. 13 girls and boys are smiling.

5. 3 girls and boys are wearing glasses.

Shopping Spree

Money

Materials:
student copies of page 102
8 small objects, every two objects
labeled with the same coin value
scissors
crayons

A student cuts apart her coin cards. Next, she looks at the price tag on each object and places a correct coin card near each one. Then she draws on her recording sheet the items that go with each money amount.

Watch Those Caps!

Subtraction to 5

Materials:
5 bottle caps in a cup
lined paper

A student empties the cup, counts the caps, and writes on his paper the total number counted. Then he subtracts the number of caps that landed faceup and solves the resulting math problem. He continues in this manner as time permits. For an added challenge, he writes a second number sentence per spill that describes the caps that landed facedown.

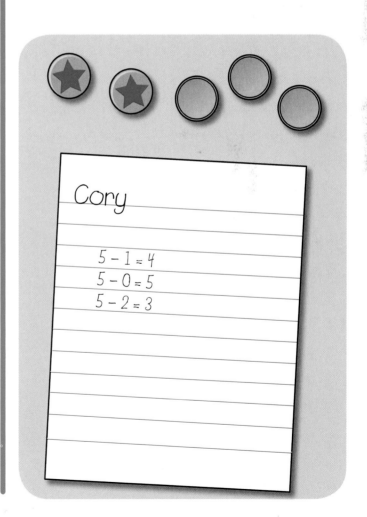

Card Categories

Sorting

Materials:
student copies of the sorting card
   recording sheet on page 101
playing cards

A youngster writes his name on his recording sheet and identifies each category. Then he sorts the playing cards as described. After each sort, he draws a check mark in the corresponding box on his paper.

Ice Cream Calculations

Addition to 12

Materials:
student copies of page 103
die

A child rolls the die and draws the corresponding number of spots (chocolate chips) on an ice cream scoop. She repeats this step for the second scoop. Then she writes on the banana a number sentence that corresponds with her scoops. She continues in this manner to complete her paper.

Funny Faces

Shapes

Materials:
pattern blocks
paper plates (one per student)
crayons

A youngster arranges pattern blocks on his paper plate to make a face. Then he names each shape as he traces it. Next, he colors the resulting facial details. For an added challenge, he labels his shapes and writes on the back of his plate the total number of each shape used.

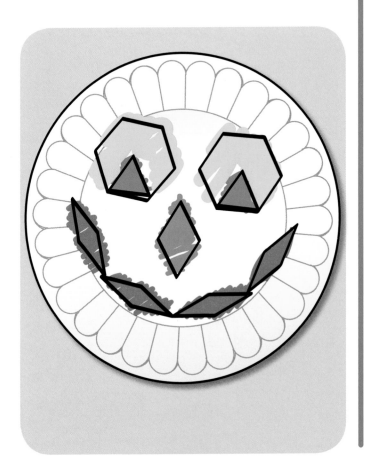

Sticky Trails

Measurement

Materials:
Unifix cubes
roll of masking tape
blank paper

A student tears a length of tape and carefully sticks it across the top of her paper. Then she uses cubes to measure its approximate length, counts the cubes, and writes the total beside the tape. She continues in this manner with more tape as time permits.

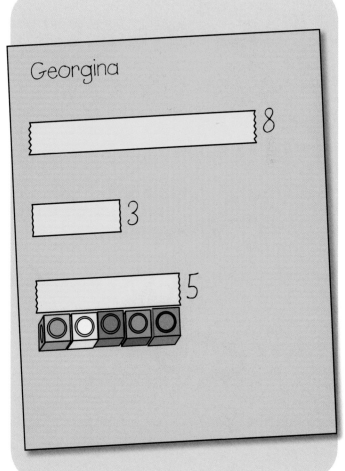

ABC Belts

Patterns

Materials:
math links

A child chooses three colors to make a belt. Then she creates a long chain with an ABC color pattern. She loops the belt around her waist and allows the leftover chain to dangle. At an appropriate time, she uses the dangling chain to tell about her chosen pattern.

Hungry Monkey

Subtraction

Materials:
copy of page 104
subtraction flash cards
yellow Unifix cubes (bananas)

A student takes a flash card and links the corresponding number of cubes (bananas) for the first number in the problem to make a banana bunch. She places the bunch near the monkey. Then she pretends to feed the monkey the number of bananas to match the second number in the problem. She counts the total number of bananas left in the bunch to solve the problem. She continues in this manner for each remaining flash card.

Coin Café

Coin values

Materials:
student copies of the coin cards on page 102
magazines
blank paper
scissors
glue

A youngster folds his paper in half and unfolds it so it resembles a menu. Next, he cuts out of a magazine eight food pictures and glues them to his paper. Then he cuts out his coin cards and glues one coin next to each food item. To complete the menu, he writes the corresponding value of each menu item.

Storybook Sort

Comparing numbers

Materials:
copy of the comparison word cards
    on page 85, cut apart
number 5 card
supply of books

A child places the word cards in her work-space to make three distinct areas. She places the number five card with the *equal to* card. Then she picks up a book and counts the number of words in the title. She places the book in the corresponding area. She continues in this manner with each remaining book.

Berry Bushes

Counting by 10s

Materials:
light green irregular circles, five per student (bushes)
long strips of paper (one per student)
red ink pad
new pencil with unused eraser
glue

A student glues five bushes on his paper strip. Then he uses the eraser and ink pad to make ten red prints (berries) on the first bush. He continues in this manner with each bush, counting aloud as he makes each print. Each time he completes a bush, he recounts by tens his total number of berries.

Stamped Headbands

Patterns

Materials:
cards programmed with pattern starters as shown
stampers
ink pads
paper strips

A child chooses a pattern starter. Using the corresponding stampers and ink pads, he copies the pattern on a paper strip. He then extends the pattern to the end of the strip. At an appropriate time, he asks to have his strip sized and stapled into a headband.

Busy All Day

Time of day

Materials:
blank paper
crayons

A youngster makes a T chart on his paper and labels the columns as shown. Then he draws pictures in the corresponding columns to show what he does during the day and at night. For an added challenge, he labels each drawn activity.

Bye-Bye, Bears

Subtraction to 10

Materials:
color spinner
10 bear counters, same colors as are on the spinner
blank paper
crayons

A student writes the total number of bears (10) on her paper. Then she spins the spinner and takes away each matching-colored bear. After she updates the math problem on her paper, she counts the total number of bears that are left and writes the difference to complete the number sentence. She continues spinning and recording in this manner as time permits.

How Many Coins?

Graphing

Materials:
student copies of page 76, programmed with title
student copies of the coin cards on page 102
number cards from 0 to 8
scissors
crayons
glue

A student cuts apart her coin cards and glues on her graph the face of a different coin to label each row. For each remaining coin card, she takes a number card and places it by the coin card. Then she colors on her graph the corresponding number of boxes for each coin. For an added challenge, she calculates each coin set's total value according to her graph.

Ten...Again!

Addition to 12

Materials:
12 two-sided counters in a bag
writing paper

A child shakes and then empties the bag. She counts the total number of counters of each color and uses the numbers to create a math problem. Then she adds the numbers to complete the number sentence. She returns the counters to the bag and continues in this manner as time permits.

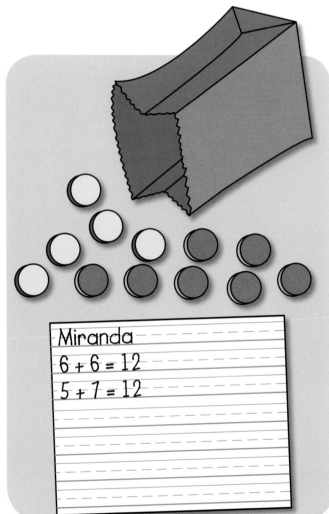

Lots of Bones

Fair shares

Materials:
6 copies of the dog pattern on page 87, cut out
24 white Unifix cubes (bones)
blank paper
crayons

A child folds and unfolds his paper to make six boxes and writes his name in the first box. Then he writes the number 2 in a box and distributes all the bones between two dog cutouts. If the total number of bones is divided evenly, he draws a happy face in the box; if not, he draws a sad face. He continues in this manner, checking for fair shares with three, four, five, and six dogs.

Rockin' Robots

Shapes

Materials:
student copies of the robot card on page 105
supply of paper shapes: triangles, squares, circles, rectangles
blank paper
scissors
glue

A student arranges shapes on her paper so they resemble a robot and then glues them in place. Then she counts the total number of each shape used and records it on her robot card. To complete the craft, she cuts out her card and glues it along the bottom of her paper.

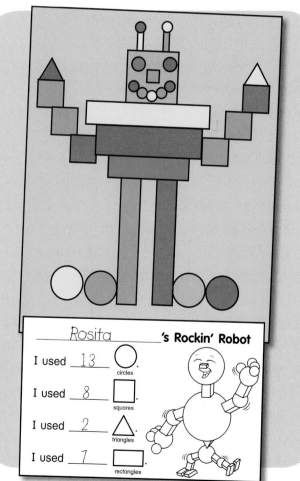

King-Size Cone

Counting by 10s

Materials:
student copies of page 106
scissors
glue

A youngster cuts out each scoop and the ice cream cone. Next, she orders the scoops by tens from top to bottom. She checks her work and then glues each piece in place above the cone. To review, she counts aloud by tens while she points to her completed cone.

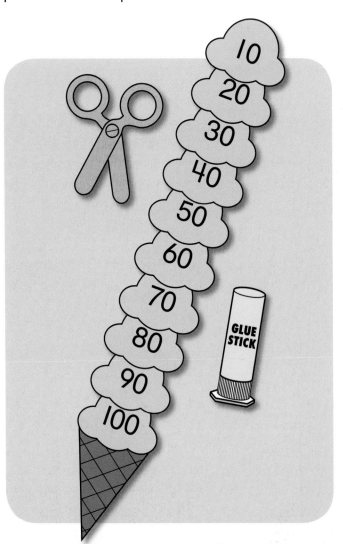

Ten Take Away...

Subtraction to 10

Materials:
number cards from 1 to 10
stampers
ink pads
small sticky notes
writing paper
blank paper

A student stamps ten prints on his blank paper. Then he takes a number card and uses sticky notes to cover the corresponding number of prints. After counting the uncovered prints, he records the number sentence on his writing paper. He removes the sticky notes and repeats the activity for each remaining card.

Dot, Dot, Ooh!

Patterns

Materials:
2 bingo daubers of different colors
pattern starter strip like the one shown
blank paper strips

To copy the pattern starter, a child makes two same-colored dots on a paper strip. Then she slides a different-colored bingo dauber to make the long ink dash. She extends the pattern to the end of her strip while chanting, "Dot, dot, ooh!" For more practice, she reverses the colors to make a different AAB pattern.

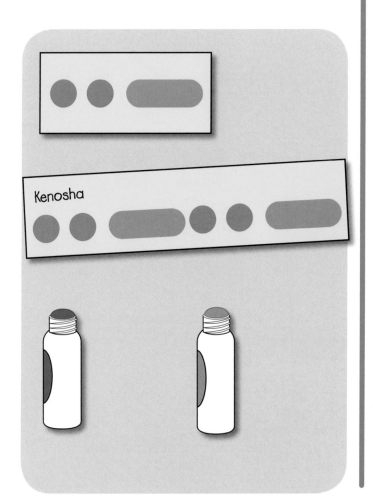

Up the Clock

Time to the hour

Materials:
copy of page 107, cut out
brown pom-pom or Unifix cube (mouse)

A student arranges the cards facedown in rows. She flips over a card and looks to see if it matches the time at the bottom of the clock. If it does, she moves the mouse onto the first space of the clock. If it does not match, she turns the card back over and chooses another card. Once the mouse is on the first space of the clock, she searches for the next matching time. She continues in this manner until the mouse reaches the top of the clock.

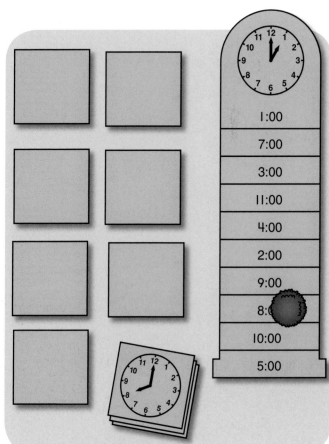

Pizza Parts

Fair shares

Materials:
circle cut into 8 equal triangles (pizza slices)
number spinner
animal counters
blank paper
crayons

A student spins the spinner and takes the corresponding number of animal counters. Then she serves the pizza, giving each animal one slice at a time, until all the slices are served. If the pizza is evenly shared, she draws her results on her paper. If not, she starts over with a new spin. She continues in this manner as time permits.

Roll 'Em

Addition to 12

Materials:
sticky dots
two dice
blank paper
crayons

A child folds and unfolds his paper to make four boxes. Next, he rolls the dice, counts the dots on each die, and sticks the same number of dots in sets on his paper. Then he writes a number sentence that corresponds with the sets of dots. He continues in this manner for each remaining box.

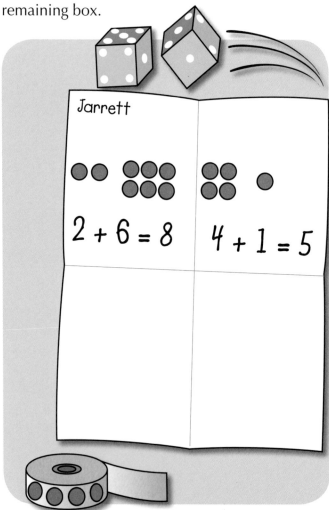

Bouncy Ball Math

Graphing

Materials:
student copies of page 76, programmed with title
student copies of the ball cards on page 105
scissors
crayons
glue

A student cuts out the cards and sorts them into four groups. To label each row on her graph, she glues one card of each ball style per row. Then she counts the total number of balls in each group and colors the corresponding number of boxes for each row. For an added challenge, she writes on the back of her paper a sentence that tells of which style there were the fewest balls.

Caterpillar Crawl

Money

Materials:
student copies of the coin cards
    on page 102, faces only
supply of penny manipulatives
12" x 18" sheets of paper (one per student)
crayons
glue

A youngster folds and unfolds his paper to make four long rows and glues a coin card at the beginning of each row as shown. Next, he places pennies in each row to show the corresponding coin value. Then he traces each row of coins to resemble an egg and three caterpillars. He adds details as desired.

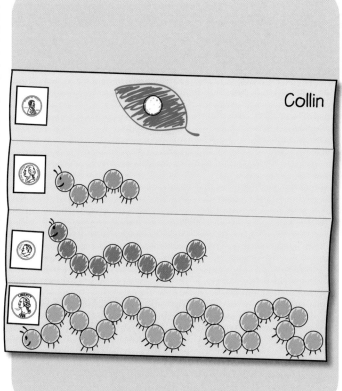

Going Buggy

Sorting

Materials:
student copies of page 108
green paper cutout (grass)
blank paper
scissors
glue

A student cuts apart his bug cards and places each one on the grass. Next, he folds his paper to make four sections, cuts apart his sorting headers, and glues one in each section. Then he sorts the bug collection and writes the number of each type under the corresponding header.

☺ happy	☹ sad
9	7

spots	stripes
10	6

legs	○ no legs
8	8

glasses	no glasses
4	12

Simply Creative

Patterns

Materials:
pattern starters similar to the ones shown
sticky dots
paper strips
crayons

A youngster sticks dots on a paper strip to copy and extend a pattern. Then she embellishes each dot with details, making sure she maintains the pattern. She continues in this manner as time permits.

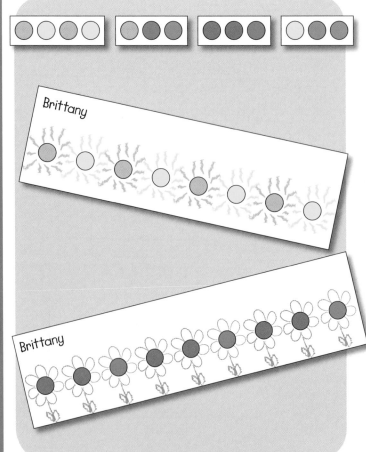

Brittany

Brittany

Minus Masterpiece

Subtraction to 10

Materials:
number cards from 6 to 10
die
paper strips
crayons

A student takes a number card and draws the corresponding number of objects on her paper strip. Next, she rolls the die. She folds one end of her paper to cover the number of objects that corresponds with the number rolled. Then she counts the remaining items to determine the difference. To finish, she writes on her paper a subtraction problem that tells about her work.

Vroom, Vroom!

Shapes

Materials:
paper shapes
blank paper
glue

A child arranges shapes on his paper so they resemble a vehicle. When satisfied, he glues them in place. Then he identifies and labels each shape. For an easier version, provide shape cards (page 78) as a reference.

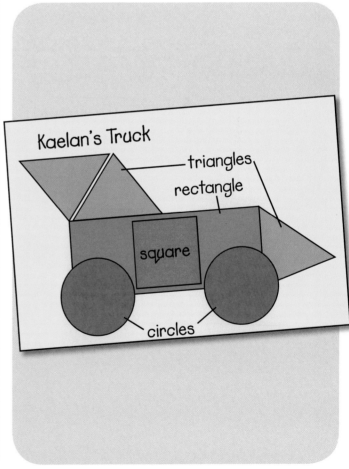

Phone Fun!

Addition to 15

Materials:
copy of page 109, cut out
cards programmed with two-letter words
blank paper

A youngster takes a card and writes the word on his paper. Next, he finds the first letter of the word on the phone and records its numerical value. Then he writes the numerical value for the second letter of the word. To finish, he adds the numbers and completes the number sentence. He continues in this manner with each remaining card.

Monthly Matchup

Calendar

Materials:
tagboard copy of page 110, cut apart

A student matches each word card to a picture card. Then she moves each matched pair, as needed, to arrange the months in order. For a personal version, she cuts out her own copy of the page and glues the pairs in order on a sheet of paper.

Halves and Wholes

Fractions

Materials:
sensory tub containing sand, rice, or water
plastic one-cup measuring cup
2 plastic half-cup measuring cups

A youngster explores parts of a whole and whole to parts by scooping and pouring the sensory-tub filler into the different measuring cups. For further exploration, provide students with teaspoons, tablespoons, and quarter cups.

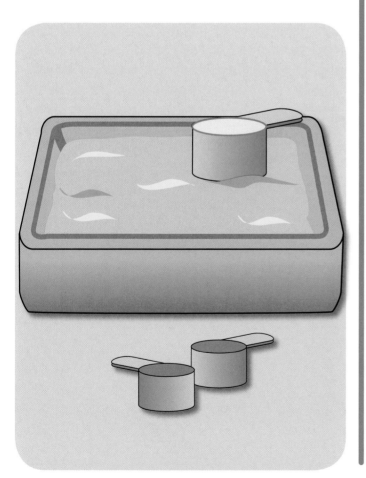

Pipefish Comparisons

Sorting

Materials:
pipe cleaners, assortment of two
    colors and two sizes (pipefish)
large sheet of blue paper (sea)

To place the pipefish in schools in the sea, a child sorts the pipefish by color. Then he re-sorts his fish by size. To make smaller schools, he sorts his schools by both attributes.

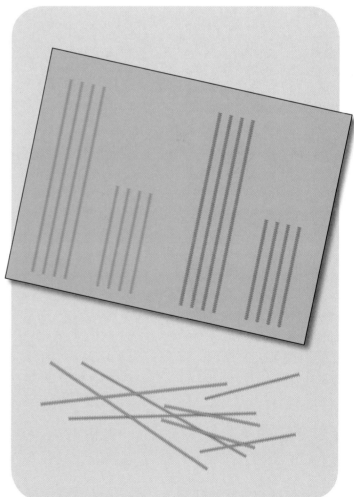

Move That Muffin!

Subtraction to 12

Materials:
muffin tin with numbered liners as shown
2 pom-poms
blank paper

A student tosses each pom-pom into a muffin cup and reads the number on each liner. Next, she identifies the larger of the two numbers, removes the liner from the tin, and writes the number on her paper. Then she subtracts the second number and records the corresponding number sentence. She continues in this manner as time permits.

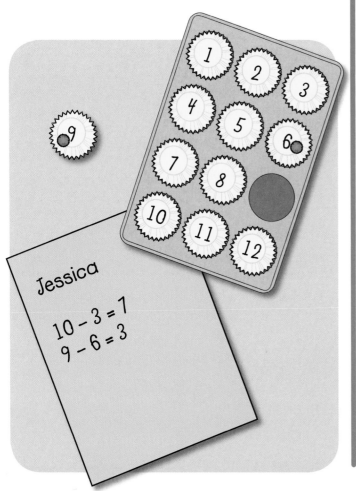

Personal Towers

Graphing

Materials:
supply of letter manipulatives
long graph labeled with letters from *A* to *Z*
writing paper

A student searches the letter supply to spell his full name. Then he places each of the letters in his name in the corresponding column on the graph. To record his findings, he writes sentences that tell about his graphed name.

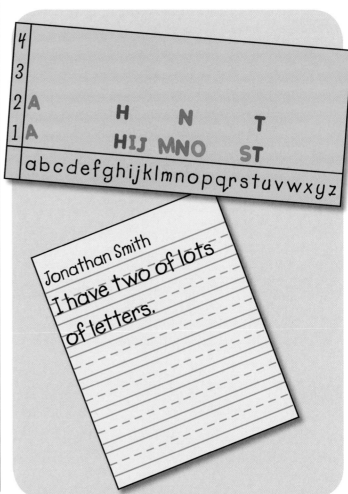

The Penny Store

Money

Materials:
objects labeled with price tags as shown
plastic penny manipulatives
blank paper
crayons

A student takes ten pennies. Then he looks at the objects and determines what he could buy with his money. He places the corresponding number of pennies by each object. When he is pleased with his selection, he draws each object and its price tag on his paper. Finally, he draws a piggy bank for his change, if any, and writes the amount.

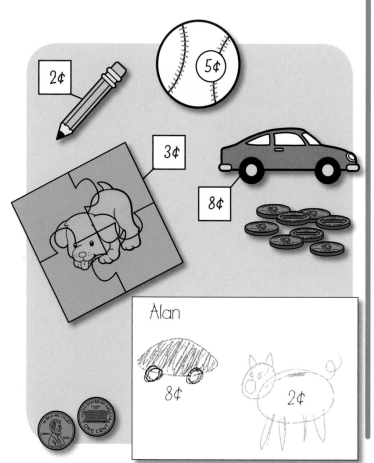

Mystery Bags

Comparing attributes

Materials:
paper lunch bags, each containing one small object
writing paper

Possible objects include a rock, a plastic lid, a stuffed animal, play dough, sandpaper, and a cotton ball.

A student randomly selects two bags. She removes the items from their bags and identifies their similarities and differences. Then she writes on her paper a sentence or two that tells about her conclusions. She continues in this manner as time permits.

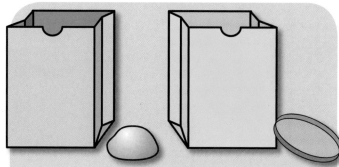

Stacie

A rock and a lid are both smooth. A rock can break something and a lid cannot.

Pie Parts

Fractions

Materials:
6 paper circles in different colors,
   cut into fractions as shown
blank paper
crayons

To explore fractions, a student places different-color circle parts together to make a whole circle. Then, for each completed circle, she traces and colors on her paper the arranged circle parts.

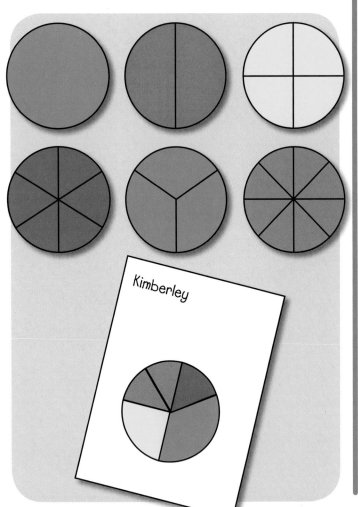

Months of the Year

Calendar

Materials:
copy of page 110, cut apart into 12 cards
12 clothespins

A youngster clips each card with a clothespin to make it stand, as shown. Then she arranges the cards in order from left to right. To check her work, she chants the names of the months as she reads the words.

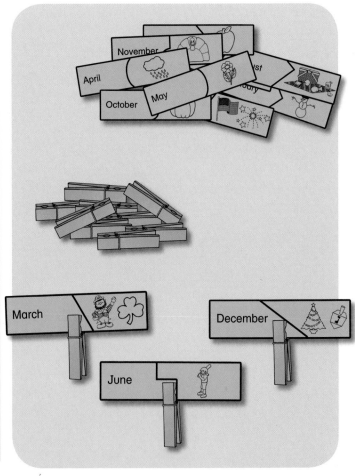

Toss and Flip!

Mixed practice

Materials:
tagboard circle (coin) labeled with "+"
    on one side and "−" on the other
large grid programmed with numbers, as shown
2 pom-poms
writing paper

A student tosses the pom-poms on the grid and then flips the coin. She uses the numbers from the grid and the operation sign from the coin to write a number sentence. She continues in this manner as time permits.

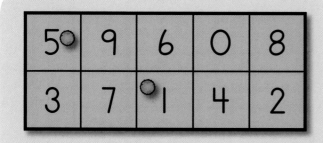

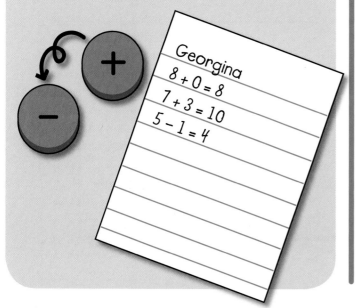

Coupon Savings

Number order

Materials:
10 coupons with different values to $1.00

A student identifies the amount on each coupon. Then she orders the coupons from least to greatest value. For an easier version, provide a hundreds chart as a reference.

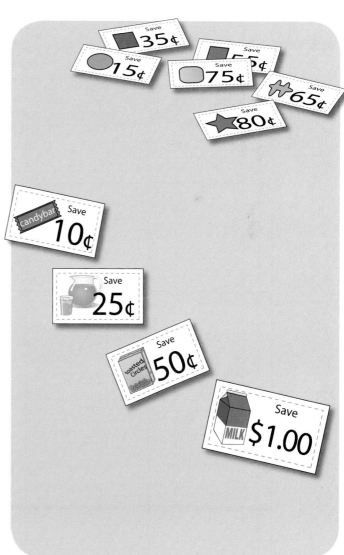

1	2	3	4	5	6	7	8

76

Super Simple Independent Practice: Math • ©The Mailbox® Books • TEC61153

Note to the teacher: Use with "How Many Socks?" on page 7, "Spinning for Colors" on page 19, "Color That Roll" on page 27, "Supreme Pizza" on page 34, "In the Pond" on page 48, "How Many Coins?" on page 62, and "Bouncy Ball Math" on page 67.

Sock Cards
Use with "How Many Socks?" on page 7.

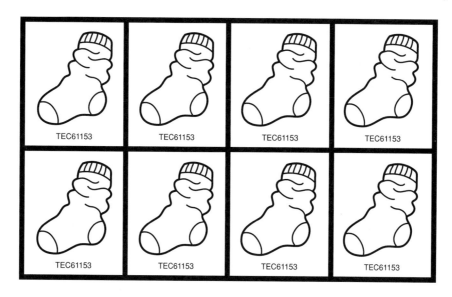

Frame Pattern
Use with "The Frame Shop" on page 8.

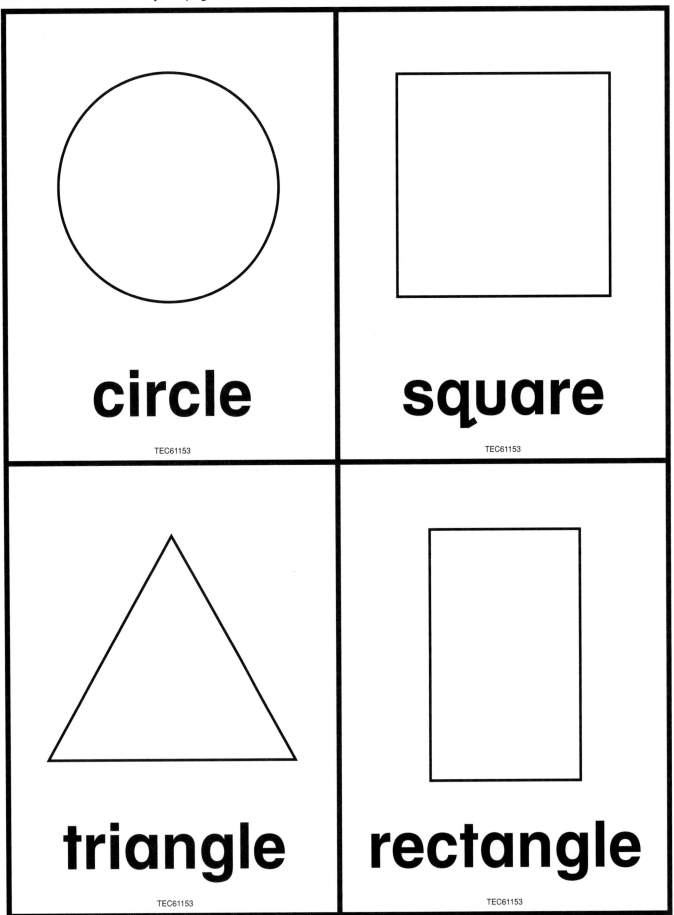

circle

TEC61153

square

TEC61153

triangle

TEC61153

rectangle

TEC61153

Super Simple Independent Practice: Math • ©The Mailbox® Books • TEC61153

Use with "Card Connections" on page 10 and "Hop on Top" on page 38.

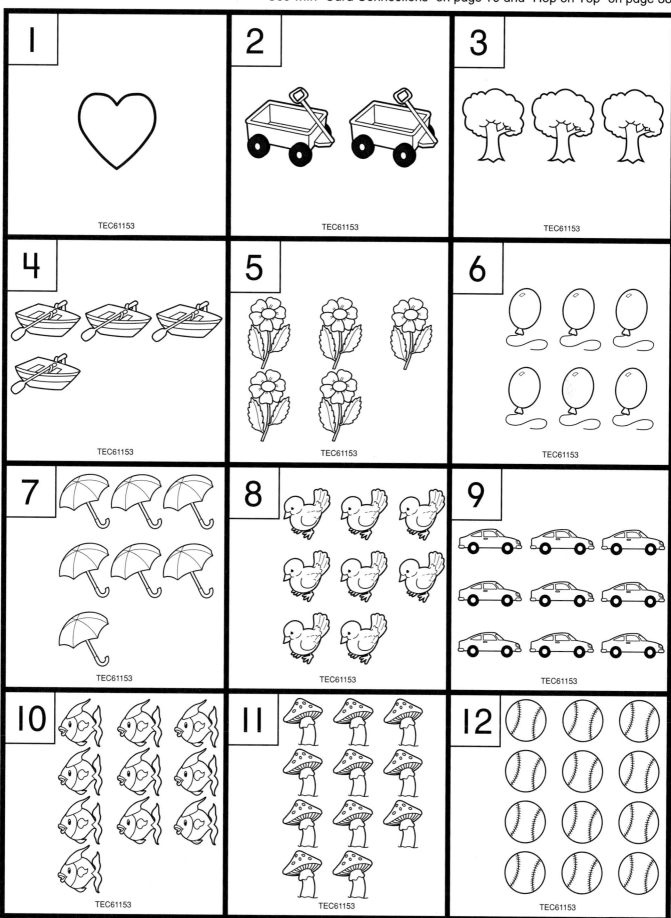

Flower Petal Patterns
Use with "Pretty Petals" on page 13.

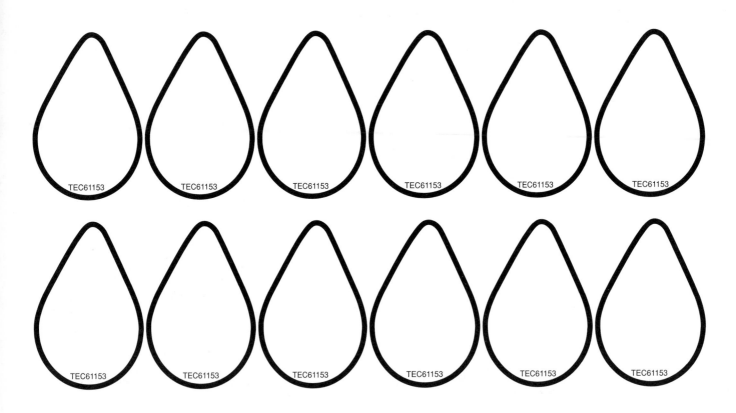

TEC61153 TEC61153 TEC61153 TEC61153 TEC61153 TEC61153

TEC61153 TEC61153 TEC61153 TEC61153 TEC61153 TEC61153

PASSPORT

Name _____

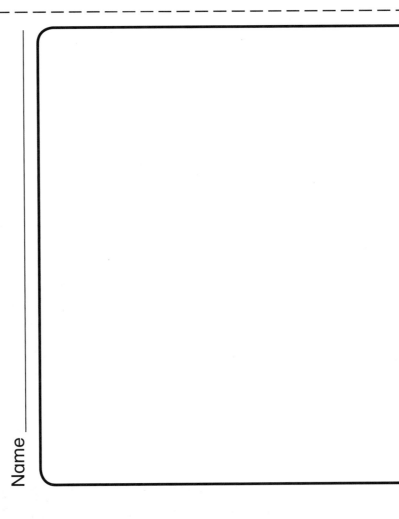

Super Simple Independent Practice: Math • ©The Mailbox® Books • TEC61153

Note to the teacher: Use with "Passport, Please!" on page 12.

Frog Cards

Use with "Happy Hoppers" on page 14 and "In the Pond" on page 48.

TEC61153

TEC61153

TEC61153

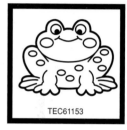

TEC61153

Flower Patterns

Use with "Little Florist" on page 15.

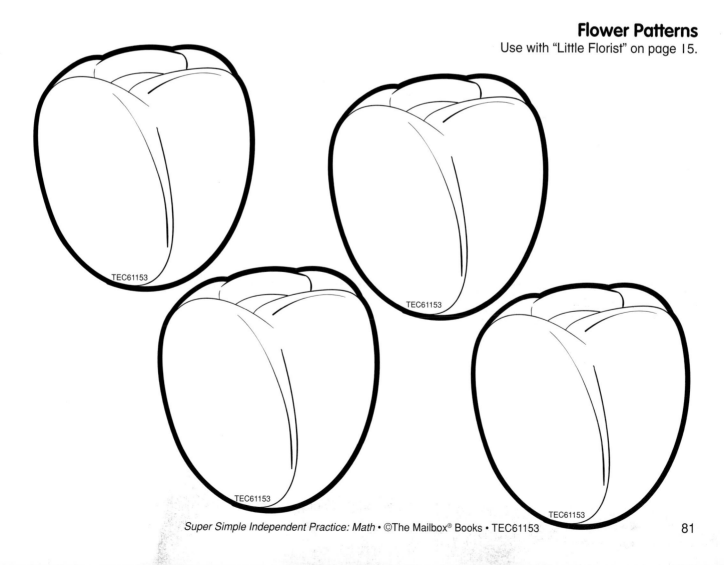

TEC61153

TEC61153

TEC61153

TEC61153

Fish Cards

Use with "In the Ocean" on page 16 and "Swimming the Distance" on page 52.

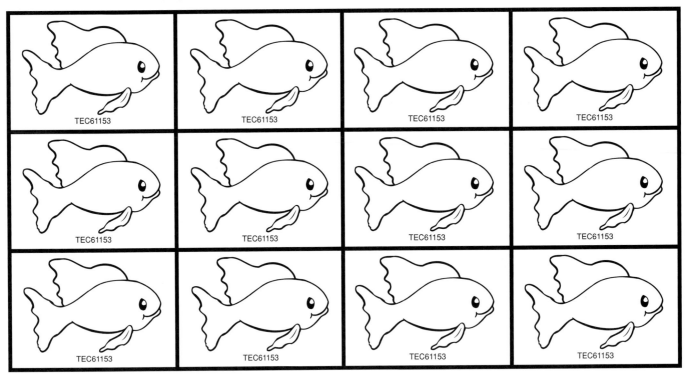

TEC61153

Name _____ Recording sheet

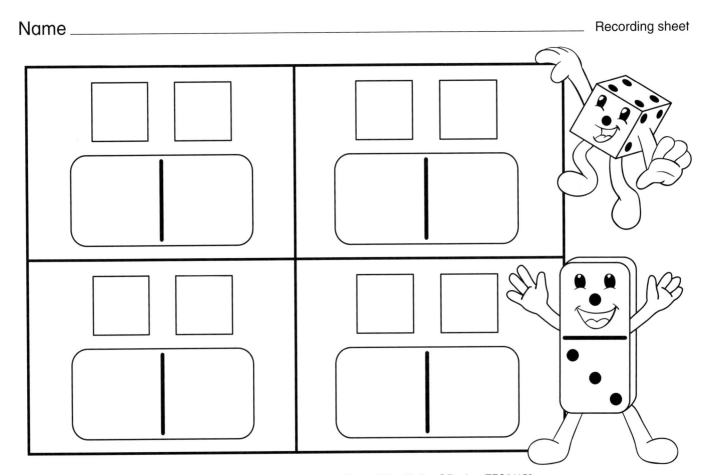

Super Simple Independent Practice: Math • ©The Mailbox® Books • TEC61153

Note to the teacher: Use with "Search and Find" on page 16.

Use with "Around the Dinosaur" on page 17 and "'Dino-mite' Designs" on page 23.

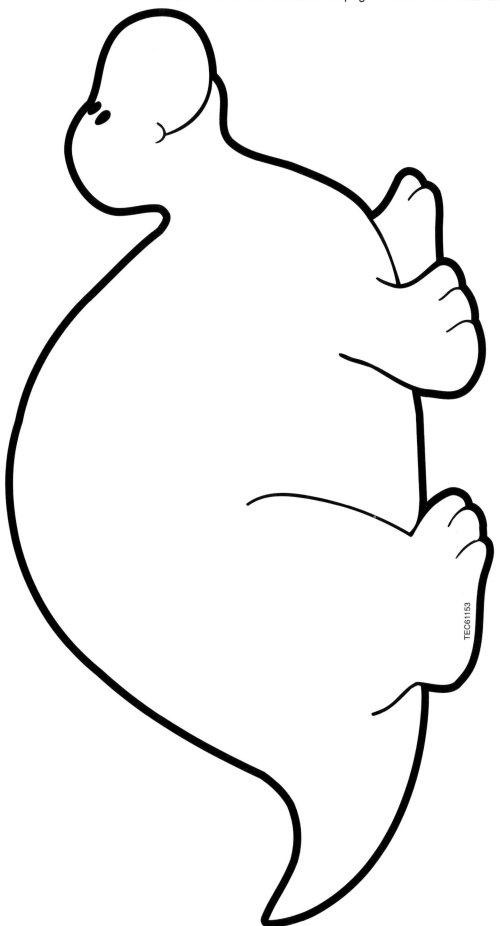

TEC61153

Muffin Pattern
Use with "Yum, Yum!" on page 17.

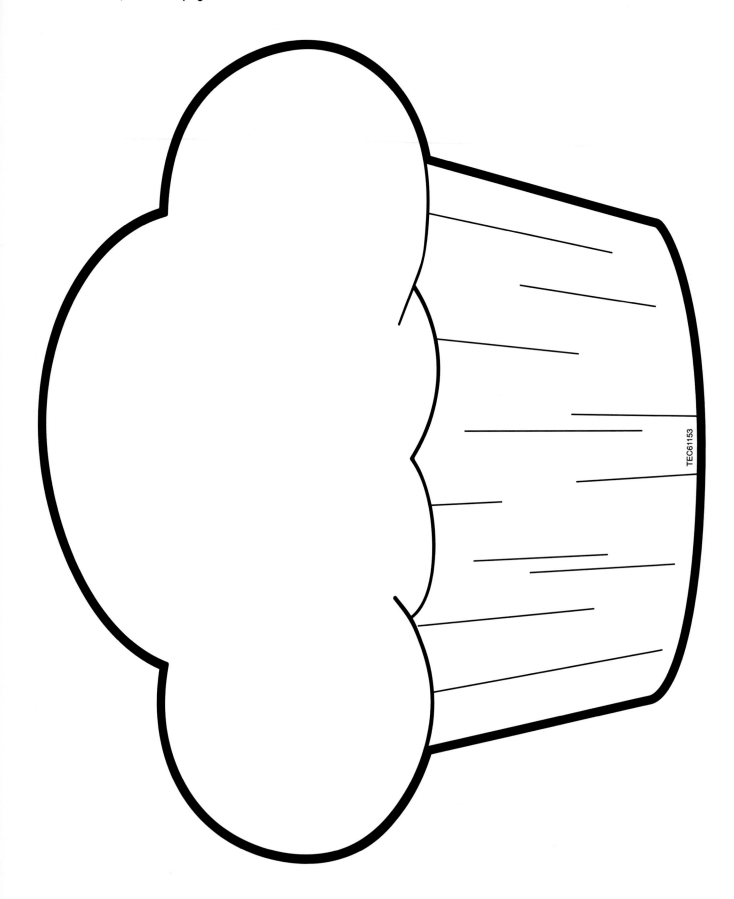

TEC61153

Super Simple Independent Practice: Math • ©The Mailbox® Books • TEC61153

Use with "More or Less" on page 20, "Here's the Scoop" on page 24, "More Spots" on page 26, "Stamps Galore!" on page 29, "Cover Up" on page 51, "A Quick Pick" on page 52, and "Storybook Sort" on page 59.

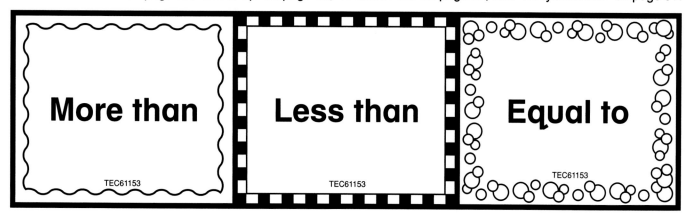

More than

TEC61153

Less than

TEC61153

Equal to

TEC61153

Name _____ Recording sheet

Happy Birthday!

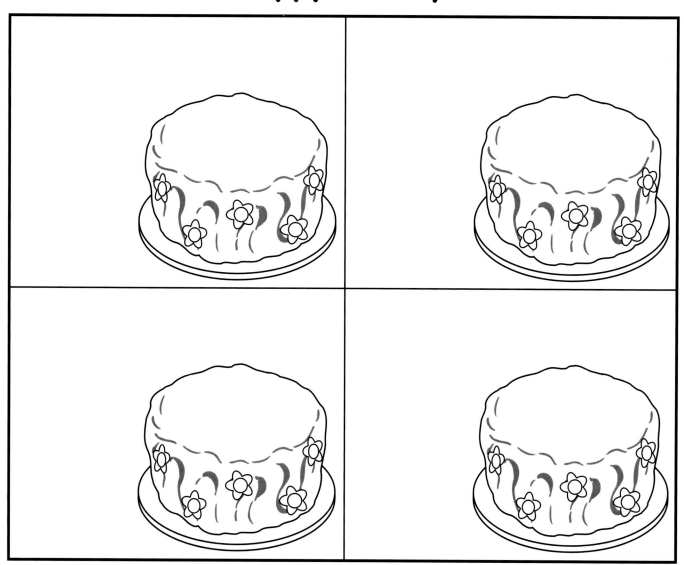

Super Simple Independent Practice: Math • ©The Mailbox® Books • TEC61153

Ocean Picture Cards
Use with "Ocean Creatures" on page 22.

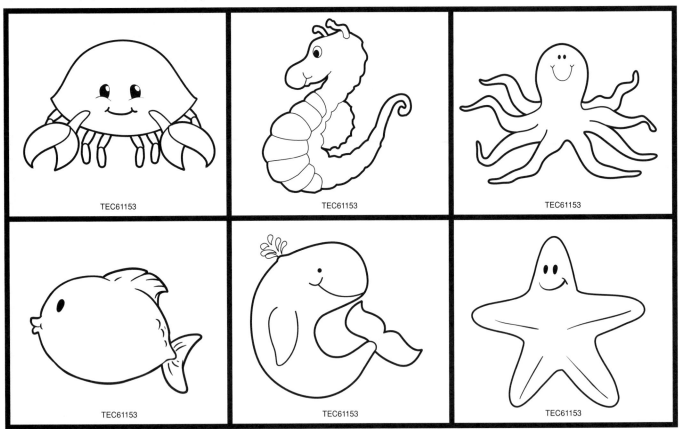

TEC61153

TEC61153

TEC61153

TEC61153

TEC61153

TEC61153

Rocket Pattern
Use with "Blast Off!" on page 25.

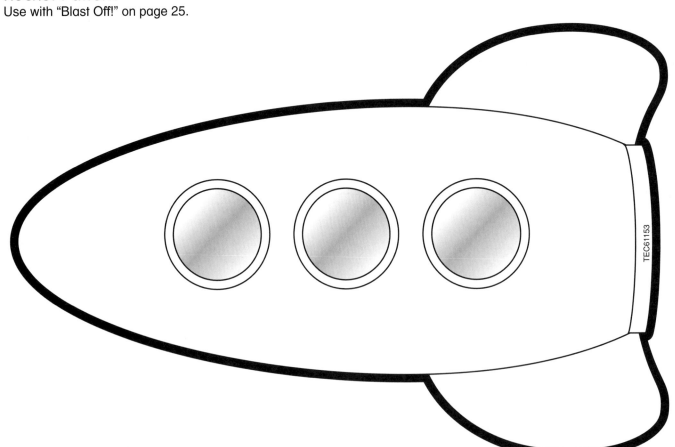

TEC61153

Dog Pattern

Use with "More Spots" on page 26, "Where Is It?" on page 31, and "Lots of Bones" on page 63.

Shell Cards

Use with "Beachcomber" on page 31.

Positional Picture Cards

Use with "Sky or Grass?" on page 27.

Super Simple Independent Practice: Math • ©The Mailbox® Books • TEC61153

Use with "Inch by Inch" on page 30.

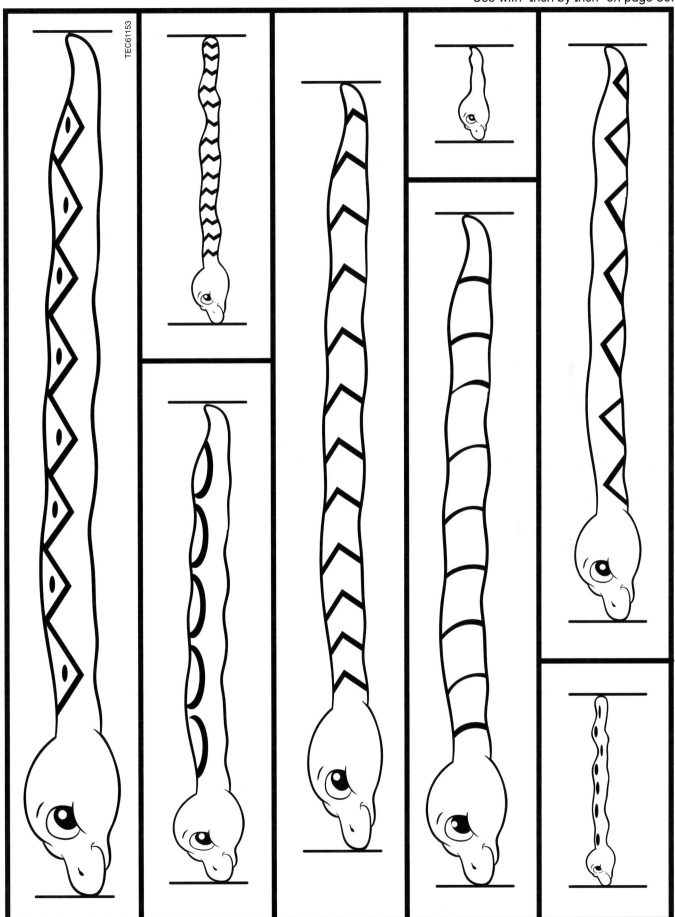

TEC61153

Seasonal Picture Cards

Use with "Savvy About Seasons" on page 30.

TEC61153

TEC61153

TEC61153

TEC61153

TEC61153

TEC61153

TEC61153

TEC61153

TEC61153

TEC61153

TEC61153

TEC61153

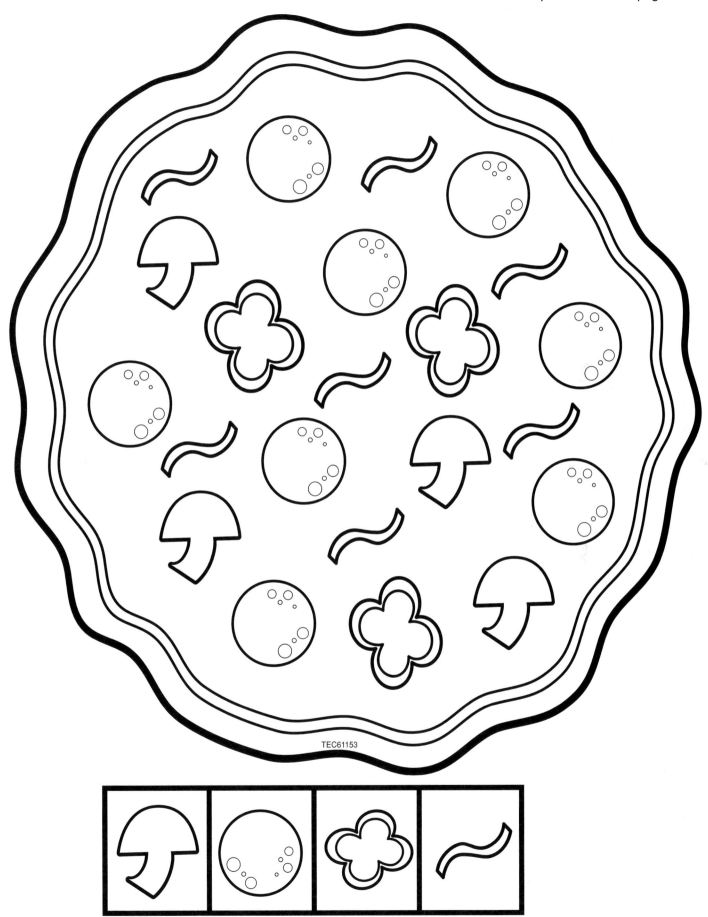

TEC61153

Gumball Machine Pattern and Recording Sheet

Use with "Gumballs Galore" on page 37.

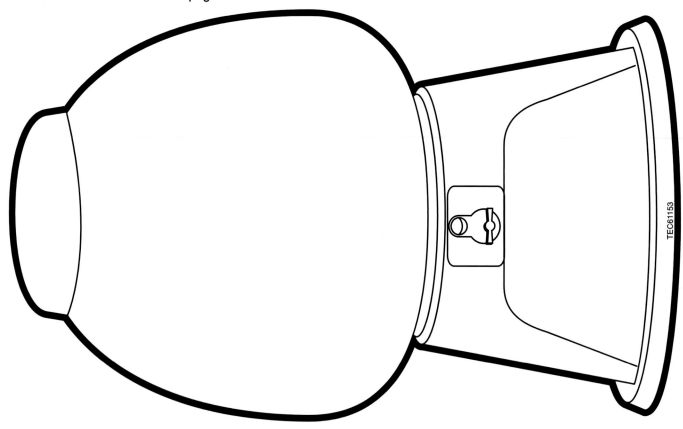

TEC61153

Name _____

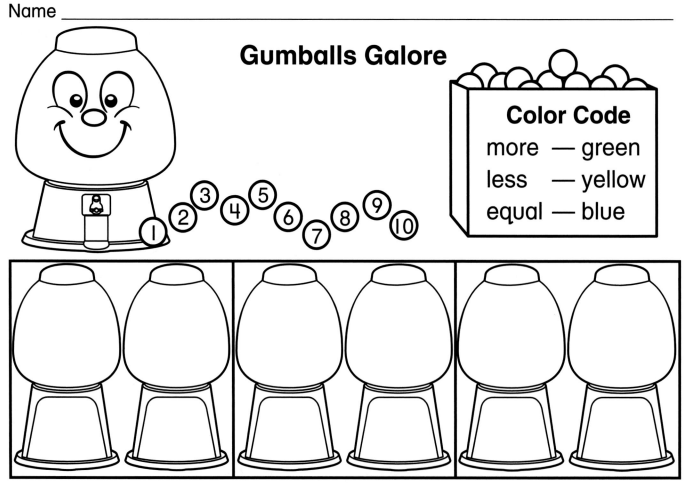

Gumballs Galore

Color Code

more — green
less — yellow
equal — blue

Fish Pattern
Use with "Fish's Bubbles" on page 39.

TEC61153

Bird Cards
Use with "Taking Flight" on page 42.

TEC61153

TEC61153

TEC61153

TEC61153

TEC61153

TEC61153

TEC61153

TEC61153

TEC61153

TEC61153

Animal Cards

Use with "Animal Travels" on page 40.

Super Simple Independent Practice: Math • ©The Mailbox® Books • TEC61153

Name _____

A Detailed Inspection

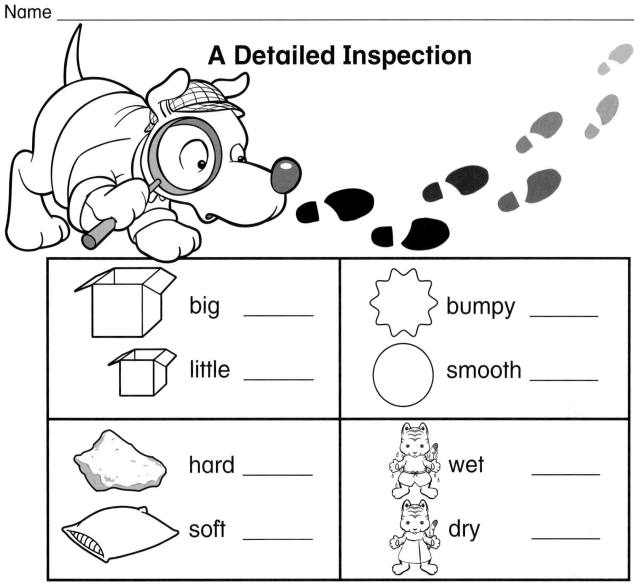

big _____		bumpy _____	
little _____		smooth _____	
hard _____		wet _____	
soft _____		dry _____	

Draw.

Note to the teacher: Use with "A Detailed Inspection" on page 41.

Super Simple Independent Practice: Math • ©The Mailbox® Books • TEC61153

96   **Note to the teacher:** Use with "Bear's Barbells" on page 43.

I like to eat
circles!

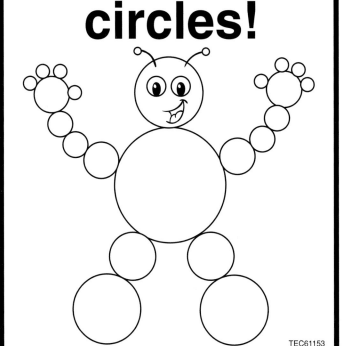

TEC61153

I like to eat
triangles!

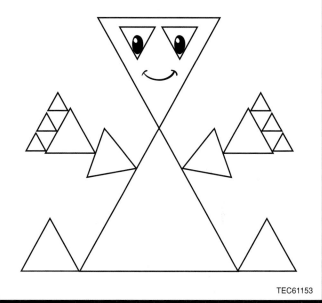

TEC61153

I like to eat
squares!

TEC61153

I like to eat
rectangles!

TEC61153

Name _____

98

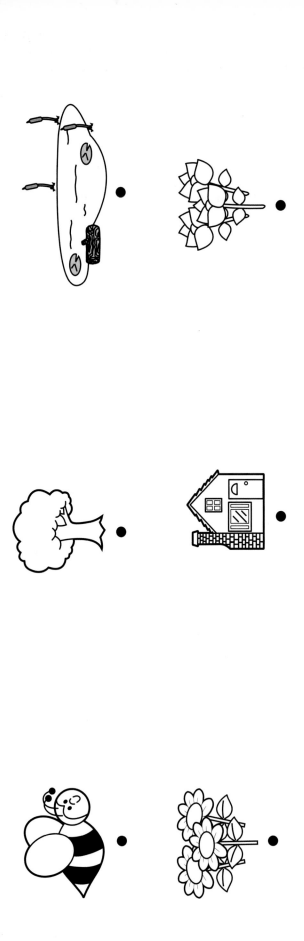

How many ?

_____ to _____

_____ to _____

_____ to _____

_____ to _____

_____ to _____

Super Simple Independent Practice: Math • ©The Mailbox® Books • TEC61153

Note to the teacher: Use with "Buzzy's Travels" on page 47.

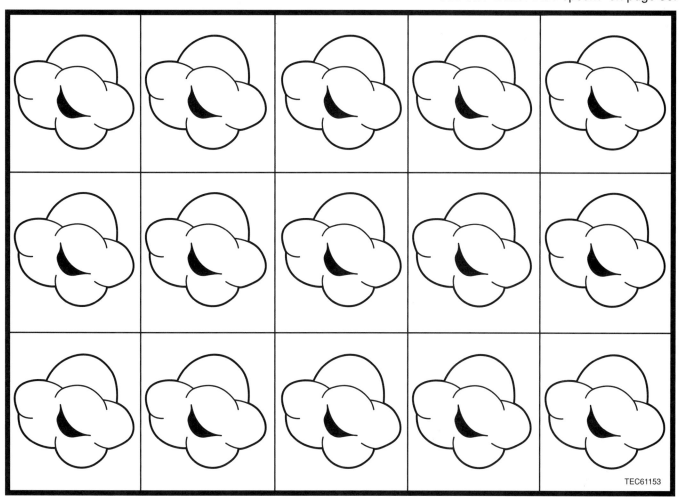

TEC61153

Shirt Patterns
Use with "On the Clothesline" on page 51.

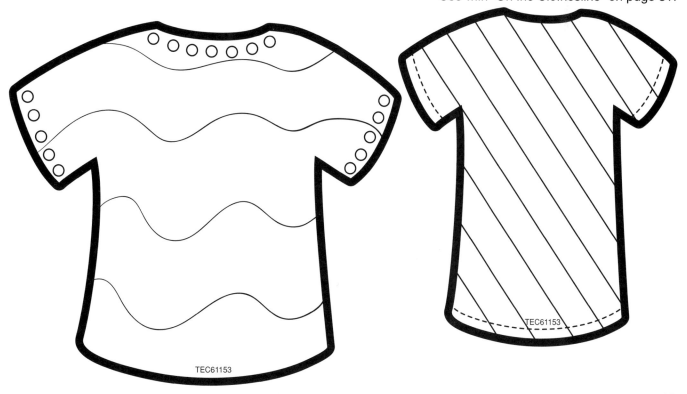

TEC61153

TEC61153

Paw Patterns
Use with "Tiny Toes" on page 54.

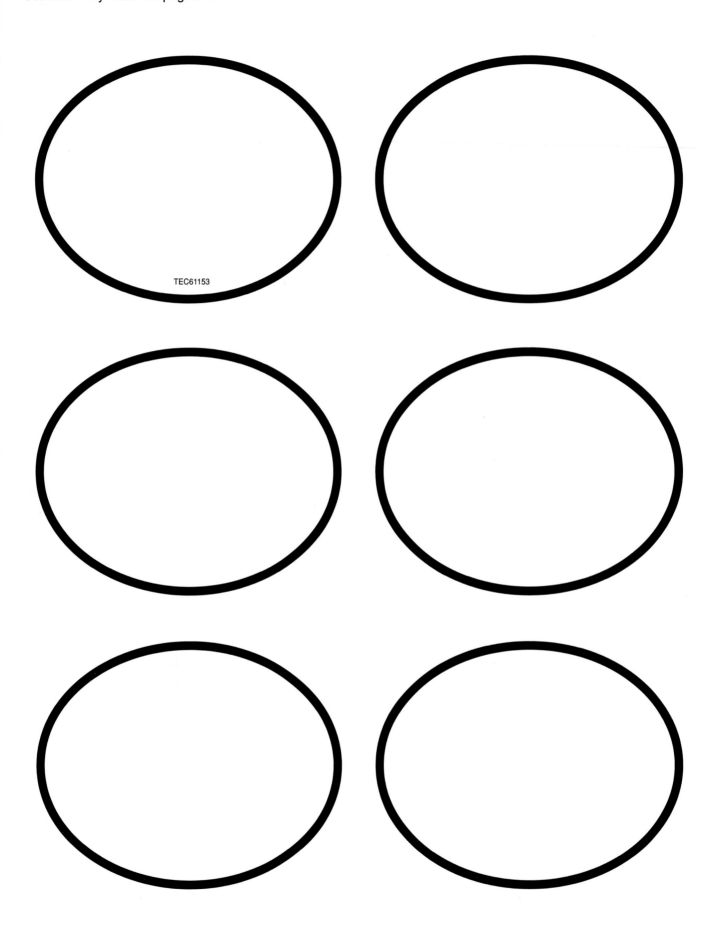

TEC61153

Super Simple Independent Practice: Math • ©The Mailbox® Books • TEC61153

1. There are _____   in the .
girls   photograph

2. There are _____   in the .
boys   photograph

3. There are _____ in the  .
teachers   photograph

4. _____  are 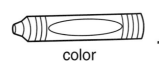 .
girls and boys   smiling

5. _____  are 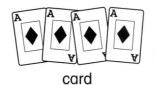 .
girls and boys   wearing glasses

Super Simple Independent Practice: Math • ©The Mailbox® Books • TEC61153

Sorting Card

I sorted by  .
color

I sorted by .
card

I sorted by .
suit

Super Simple Independent Practice: Math • ©The Mailbox® Books • TEC61153

Note to the teacher: Use the sentence recording sheet with "A Photo Finish" on page 54. Use the sorting card recording sheet with "Card Categories" on page 56.

Coin Cards

Use with "Shopping Spree" on page 55, "Coin Café" on page 59, "How Many Coins?" on page 62, and "Caterpillar Crawl" on page 67.

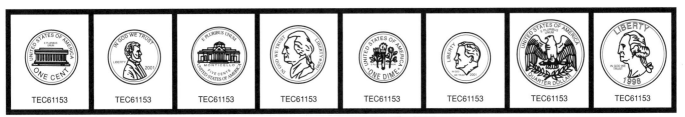

Name _____ Recording sheet

Shopping Spree

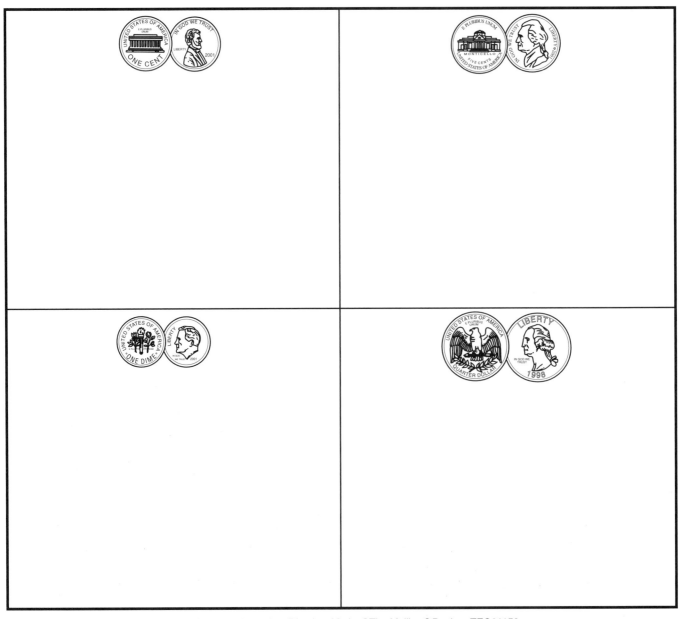

Super Simple Independent Practice: Math • ©The Mailbox® Books • TEC61153

102   **Note to the teacher:** Use with "Shopping Spree" on page 55.

Super Simple Independent Practice: Math • ©The Mailbox® Books • TEC61153

Note to the teacher: Use with "Hungry Monkey" on page 58.

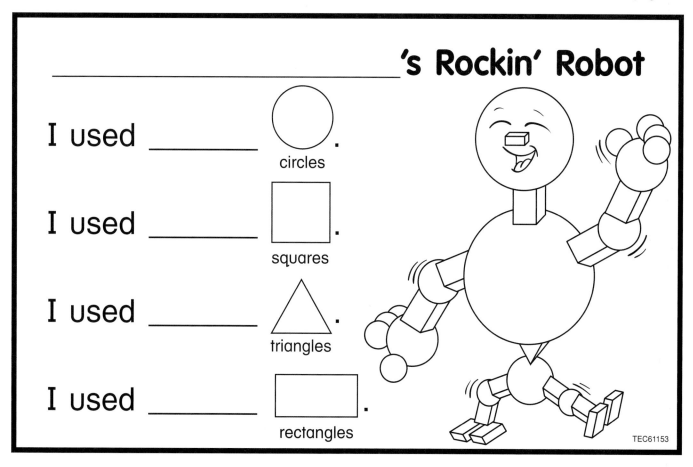

_____'s **Rockin' Robot**

I used _____ ◯.
circles

I used _____ ▢.
squares

I used _____ △.
triangles

I used _____ ▭.
rectangles

TEC61153

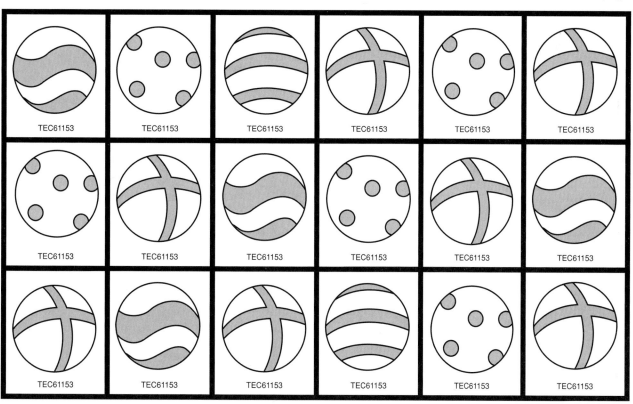

TEC61153   TEC61153   TEC61153   TEC61153   TEC61153   TEC61153

TEC61153   TEC61153   TEC61153   TEC61153   TEC61153   TEC61153

TEC61153   TEC61153   TEC61153   TEC61153   TEC61153   TEC61153

Ice Cream Scoop and Cone Patterns
Use with "King-Size Cone" on page 64.

Super Simple Independent Practice: Math •©The Mailbox® Books • TEC61153

1:00

7:00

3:00

11:00

4:00

2:00

9:00

8:00

10:00

5:00

Bug Cards and Sorting Headers
Use with "Going Buggy" on page 68.

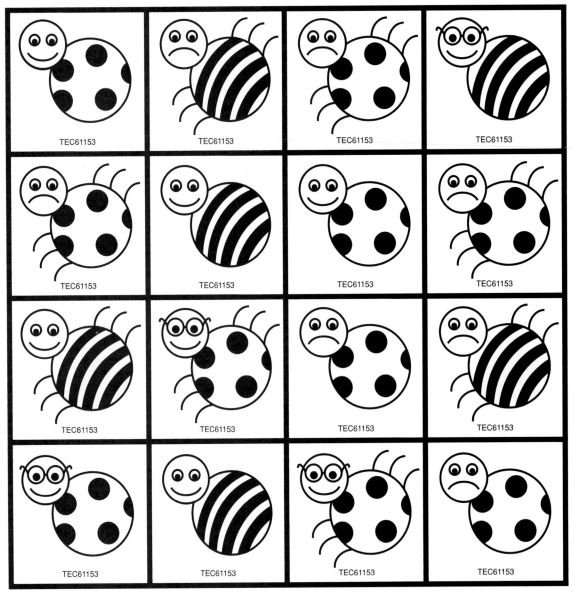

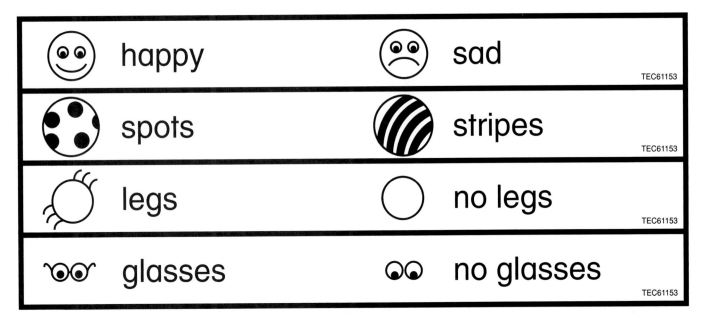

Super Simple Independent Practice: Math • ©The Mailbox® Books • TEC61153

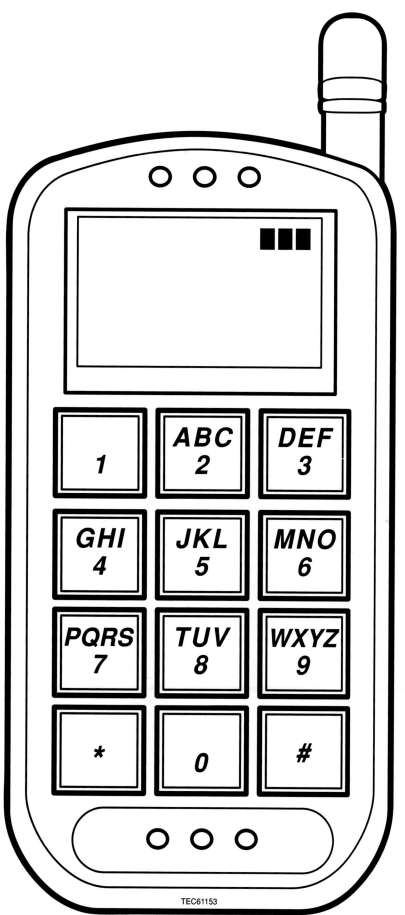

TEC61153

Month Cards

Use with "Monthly Matchup" on page 70 and "Months of the Year" on page 74.

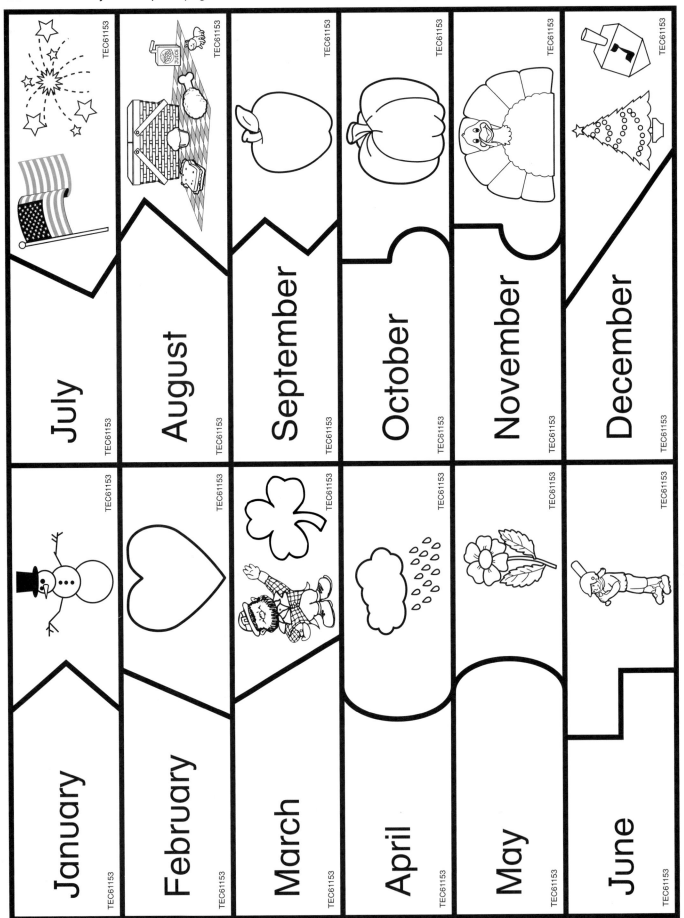

July — TEC61153

August — TEC61153

September — TEC61153

October — TEC61153

November — TEC61153

December — TEC61153

January — TEC61153

February — TEC61153

March — TEC61153

April — TEC61153

May — TEC61153

June — TEC61153

Super Simple Independent Practice: Math • ©The Mailbox® Books • TEC61153

Skills Index

Patterning & Algebra